Working Words in
SPELLING

G. Willard Woodruff and George N. Moore
with Robert G. Forest • Richard A. Talbot • Ann R. Talbot

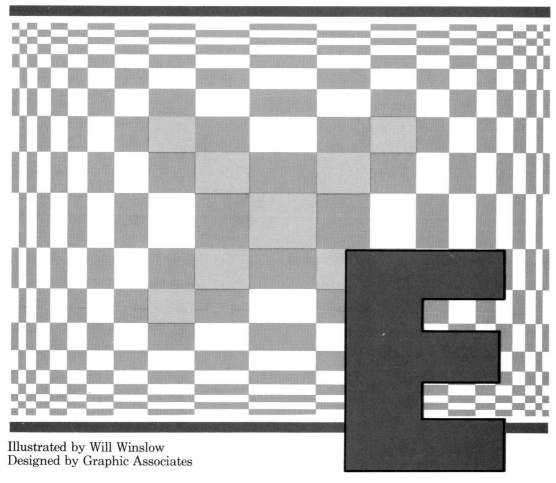

Illustrated by Will Winslow
Designed by Graphic Associates

D.C. Heath and Company
Lexington, Massachusetts/Toronto, Canada

Become a S-H-A-R-P Speller

See the word.
- Look at the word.
- Think about the letters that spell the word.

Hear the word.
- Say the word.
- Listen to the consonant and vowel sounds.

Adopt the word.
- Close your eyes.
- See the word in your mind's eye.
- Think about how it looks and sounds.

Record the word.
- Cover the word.
- Write the word.

Proofread the word.
- Correct the word.
- Touch each letter.
- Think about the word again.

SPELLEX®—a registered trademark of Curriculum Associates, Inc.
SPELLEX® Glossary incorporated by permission of Curriculum Associates, Inc.
Handwriting models in this book are reproduced with permission of Zaner-Bloser, Inc., from the series *HANDWRITING: Basic Skills and Application,* ©1984.

International Standard Book Number: 0-669-15458-X

1 2 3 4 5 6 7 8 9 0

Lesson 1

I. Check Test. Write each spelling word.

II. Spelling Words and Phrases

grace	moves with **grace**
graze	to **graze** in the meadow
whale	protecting the **whale**
brake	tightened the **brake**
operate	to **operate** the machines
mistake	without a **mistake**
escape	to **escape** from danger
grapes	a bunch of **grapes**
safely	drove **safely**
crazy	a **crazy** day
break	to **break** a dish
greatest	the **greatest** animal
fare	paid a full **fare**
bare	running in **bare** feet
rare	an extremely **rare** gem
scare	wouldn't **scare** me
square	each corner of the **square**
compare	to **compare** prices
preparing	**preparing** a meal
scarce	a **scarce** supply

III. Find a Fit. Write each word in its correct shape.

a.
b.
c.
d.
e.
f.
g.
h.
i.
j.
k.
l.
m.
n.
o.
p.
q.
r.
s.
t.

Other Word Forms

graces, graceful, grazes, grazing, whaling, whaler, braking, operates, operating, mistakes, mistaken, mistaking, escaped, escaping, grape, safe, safest, craziest, crazily, broke, breaking, great, greatly, fares, faring, barely, barest, rarer, rarest, rarely, scared, scaring, scary, squarest, squarely, comparing, comparison, prepare, preparation, scarcest, scarcely

3

IV. Base Words. The spelling list contains sixteen base words and four words with suffixes. Write each spelling word.

Words With Suffixes	Base Words
a. scary	_____
b. whaler	_____
c. operating	_____
d. escaped	_____
e. breaking	_____
f. craziest	_____
g. comparison	_____
h. scarcely	_____
i. rarer	_____
j. barely	_____
k. mistaken	_____
l. braking	_____
m. graceful	_____
n. squarely	_____
o. grazing	_____
p. fares	_____
q. _____	prepare
r. _____	safe
s. _____	great
t. _____	grape

4

Spelling Words

grace graze whale brake operate mistake escape
grapes safely crazy break greatest fare bare
rare scare square compare preparing scarce

V. Context Clues. Using only words on the spelling list, solve the word mysteries. If you need help, use the **Glossary/SPELLEX®**.

a. These gems are expensive. They must be _____ .

b. You must pay a fee to ride the bus. You must pay a _____ .

c. The baby is unclothed. He is _____ .

d. He worked all morning. He was entitled to a _____ .

e. Jumping from a high place could be frightening. It may _____ you.

f. The prisoner cannot be found. Did he _____ ?

g. I shouldn't have opened the letter. That was my _____ .

h. Some mammals live in the sea. One of them is the _____ .

i. These cows need a large meadow. They must _____ .

j. They're used for making raisins. They must be _____ .

k. This rectangle has equal sides. It must be a _____ .

l. Use the floor pedal to stop the car. Use the _____ .

m. The skater glides smoothly over the ice. She has _____ .

n. The doctor is going to remove my appendix. She must _____ .

o. Be careful crossing the street. Please walk _____ .

p. My spaniel chases his tail. Sometimes I think my dog is _____ .

q. The chef enjoys cooking. What is he _____ now?

r. There are many great wonders in the world. The pyramids in Egypt are

   the _____ .

s. The twins are different in many ways. Why do people _____ them?

t. There are only a few of these birds around. They are _____ .

5

VI. Homophones. Write the homophone from the spelling list that matches each word below.

Words	Homophones
a. bear	_____
b. wail	_____
c. fair	_____
d. break	_____
e. grays	_____

VII. Generally Speaking. Write a spelling word in the group it best fits. You may wish to use the **Glossary/SPELLEX®** to look up the meanings of *rare* and *scarce*.

a. frighten, terrify, _____

b. mammal, porpoise, _____

c. circle, rectangle, _____

d. oranges, apples, _____

e. poise, manners, _____

f. cautiously, carefully, _____

g. error, misprint, _____

h. dwindling, few, _____

i. making, cooking, _____

j. best, biggest, _____

k. unusual, unique, _____

l. insane, foolish, _____

m. getaway, exit, _____

n. match, study, _____

o. smash, crack, _____

p. control, run, _____

VIII. Book List. Using all of the spelling words, make up titles for books. You may use **Other Word Forms** (p. 3). Circle the spelling words and the other word forms you used.

Example: *The (Great) (Escaping) (Whale)*

IX. Final Test. Write each spelling word.

Lesson 2

I. Check Test. Write each spelling word.

II. Spelling Words and Phrases

beam	a **beam** of light
seal	will **seal** the envelope
heap	a **heap** of trash
cheat	caught the **cheat**
peace	a lasting **peace**
preach	heard you **preach**
reason	one good **reason**
ideal	an **ideal** day
easy	**easy** to use
dealing	**dealing** the cards
reaches	**reaches** the top
reached	**reached** the prize
eastern	on the **eastern** slope
really	if it **really** matters
beaten	the **beaten** team
meantime	in the **meantime**
meanwhile	in the **meanwhile**
seashore	walked along the **seashore**
we've	whatever **we've** done
we're	if **we're** going

III. Find a Fit. Write each word in its correct shape.

a.
b.
c.
d.
e.
f.
g.
h.
i.
j.
k.
l.
m.
n.
o.
p.
q.
r.
s.
t.

Other Word Forms
beamed, beaming, sealed, sealing, heaped, cheated, cheater, peaceful, preaches, preaching, reasoned, reasonable, ideals, ideally, easier, easiest, deal, dealt, dealer, reach, reaching, east, easterner, real, realize, beat, beating, beater, seashores

7

IV. Recycle.

a. Write each of the spelling words in the correct box. A word may be used more than once.

Words With Only Two Consonants

1. _____   5. _____
2. _____   6. _____
3. _____   7. _____
4. _____

Base Words With Suffixes

1. _____
2. _____
3. _____
4. _____
5. _____
6. _____

Words With ch, wh, sh, st, and ng

1. _____   5. _____
2. _____   6. _____
3. _____   7. _____
4. _____   8. _____

Words That Are Contractions

1. _____   2. _____

Compound Words

1. _____
2. _____
3. _____

b. What words are used more than once?

1. _____   3. _____   5. _____   7. _____
2. _____   4. _____   6. _____   8. _____

c. What two words are not used?

1. _____   2. _____

Spelling Words

beam seal heap cheat peace preach reason
ideal easy dealing reaches reached eastern really
beaten meantime meanwhile seashore we've we're

V. Hide and Seek. The spelling words and some **Other Word Forms** (p. 7) can be found in the word puzzle. The words appear across, down, and diagonally. Circle and write the words.

Spelling Words

Across

1.
2.
3.
4.
5.
6.
7.
8.
9.
10.
11.
12.
13.
14.
15.
16.
17.

Down

1.
2.

Diagonally

1.

Other Word Forms

Across

1.
2.
3.
4.
5.

Down

1.
2.
3.
4.
5.

```
p e a c e r e a l l y b e o
v m w e r e n s e a l e d p
i d e a l e a s t e r n n e
d d e a l o d e a l i n g a
h e a p n r e a c h e d b c
p e i c h w c b e a t h e e
r e a s o n h b e a m e a f
e e a s y l e i w e r a t u
a w e v x a a l l e p e l
c r c h e a t e r e a e n e
h s e a s h o r e m l d r a
i s e a l m e a n t i m e s
n n o r t r e a c h i n g t
g r e a c h e s p r e a c h
```

VI. Crossword Puzzle.

a. Solve the puzzle by using eighteen words from the spelling list. Check your answers in the **Glossary/SPELLEX®**.

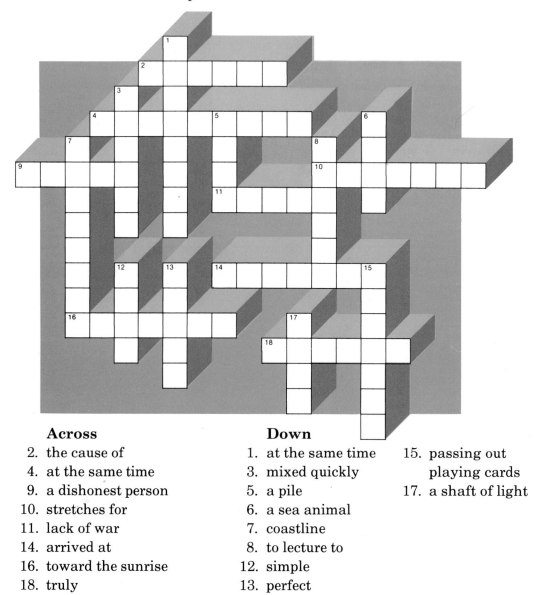

Across

2. the cause of
4. at the same time
9. a dishonest person
10. stretches for
11. lack of war
14. arrived at
16. toward the sunrise
18. truly

Down

1. at the same time
3. mixed quickly
5. a pile
6. a sea animal
7. coastline
8. to lecture to
12. simple
13. perfect

15. passing out playing cards
17. a shaft of light

b. Complete the sentence below by using the two spelling words that were not in the puzzle.

_____ going to get ice cream after _____ finished supper.

VII. Final Test. Write each spelling word.

Lesson 3

I. Check Test. Write each spelling word.

II. Spelling Words and Phrases

rise	saw the balloon **rise**
guide	will **guide** the way
invite	wanted to **invite**
decide	will **decide** on a color
divide	to **divide** by seven
finest	the **finest** piece of work
ninth	the **ninth** inning
lining	the **lining** of my jacket
filing	**filing** the letters
knives	sharpened the **knives**
lively	a **lively** game
item	counted each **item**
final	the **final** race
dried	a box of **dried** fruit
tied	**tied** the ribbon
I'd	if **I'd** tried
I'll	because **I'll** be there
I've	since **I've** started
hadn't	**hadn't** gone
doesn't	**doesn't** have to go

III. Find a Fit. Write each word in its correct shape.

a.
b.
c.
d.
e.
f.
g.
h.
i.
j.
k.
l.
m.
n.
o.
p.
q.
r.
s.
t.

Other Word Forms

rises, rose, rising, risen, guided, guiding, invites, invited, inviting, decides, decided, deciding, divides, divided, dividing, fine, finer, nine, line, lines, lined, file, filed, knife, knifed, live, livelier, liveliest, items, itemize, finally, finalist, dry, dries, drying, drier, tie, ties, tying

IV. Sentence Detective. Unscramble the scrambled word to find the spelling word that completes the sentence. Write the word.

	Scrambled Words
a. Who will _____ where to go?	dicdee
b. I passed the _____ exam.	lafin
c. Every tour is led by a _____ .	digue
d. _____ the crayons among the children.	diveid
e. The laundry _____ rapidly.	deidr
f. This rope is _____ too tightly.	deit
g. Use both forks and _____ .	knevis
h. I enjoy _____ , fun-loving people.	vyllie
i. _____ your friends to the party.	vintie
j. Does the sun _____ in the east?	esir
k. Each _____ must be priced for the sale.	temi
l. Give the teacher only your _____ work.	stifen
m. She placed _____ in the marathon.	thinn
n. The tailor sewed the _____ of his coat.	ingnil
o. The secretary enjoys _____ and typing.	lingif

V. Let's Talk. Complete the conversation below by using the correct contractions from the spelling list.

a. Arthur: (I have) _____ seen that person before.

b. Police officer: He (does not) _____ match the description of the jewel thief.

c. Police officer: (Had not) _____ you better take a closer look?

d. Arthur: (I had) _____ better.

e. Police officer: (I will) _____ bring him down to the station for questioning.

Spelling Words

*rise guide invite decide divide finest ninth
lining filing knives lively item final dried
tied I'd I'll I've hadn't doesn't*

VI. All in a Row. Write the twenty spelling words in alphabetical order.
Then join the boxed letters and write four hidden words.

1. ☐ _ _ ☐ _ _
2. _ _ ☐ ☐ _ _
3. ☐ _ _ _ _ _
4. _ _ ☐ _ _ _
5. _ _ _ _ ☐ ☐

Hidden Word: _____

6. _ ☐ _ _ _
7. _ _ ☐ _ _ ☐
8. _ _ _ _ ☐
9. _ _ _ ☐ _
10. _ ☐

Hidden Word: _____

11. _ ' _ ☐
12. ☐ _ _ _ _ _
13. _ _ _ ☐
14. _ ' _ _
15. _ _ _ _ _ _ ☐

Hidden Word: _____

16. _ ☐ _ _ ☐ _
17. _ _ ☐ _ _ _
18. _ ☐ _ ☐ _
19. _ _ _ ☐
20. _ _ _ ☐

Hidden Word: _____

VII. Arrange and Change. Rearrange the word squares and write the five
contractions from the spelling list.

| I | had | will | have | does | not |

Two Words		**Contractions**
1. _____ _____	=	_____
2. _____ _____	=	_____
3. _____ _____	=	_____
4. _____ _____	=	_____
5. _____ _____	=	_____

VIII. Base Words. The spelling list contains seven base words and eight words with suffixes. Write each word.

Words With Suffixes	Base Words	Words With Suffixes	Base Words
a. finally	_____	h. _____	nine
b. items	_____	i. _____	line
c. guiding	_____	j. _____	tie
d. deciding	_____	k. _____	fine
e. invited	_____	l. _____	live
f. dividing	_____	m. _____	file
g. rises	_____	n. _____	dry
		o. _____	knife

IX. All in a Sentence. Write all of the spelling words in sentences. Use as many **Other Word Forms** (p. 11) as you can. Circle the spelling words and the other word forms you used.

X. Final Test. Write each spelling word.

14

I. Check Test. Write each spelling word.

II. Spelling Words and Phrases

hose	the garden **hose**
whole	ate it **whole**
jokes	tells **jokes**
tones	**tones** of the bells
votes	**votes** for the mayor
chosen	had **chosen** the ripe melon
frozen	a **frozen** lake
lonely	a **lonely** task
lonesome	**lonesome** and homesick
don't	if we **don't** care
ore	mined the **ore**
bore	to **bore** through the plank
border	around the **border**
forbid	to **forbid** talking
scorn	will **scorn** and reject
northern	a **northern** state
formed	**formed** a straight line
ordered	**ordered** them to stop
orchard	a peach **orchard**
forward	looking **forward**

III. Find a Fit. Write each word in its correct shape.

a.
b.
c.
d.
e.
f.
g.
h.
i.
j.
k.
l.
m.
n.
o.
p.
q.
r.
s.
t.

Other Word Forms

hoses, hosed, hosing, wholly, joke, joker, joking, tone, toned, toning, voter, voting, choose, chose, choosing, freeze, freezes, freezing, froze, lone, lonelier, loneliest, ores, bores, bored, boring, bordered, forbidden, scorned, scornful, northerner, forming, formal, order, orchards, forwardness

15

IV. Find the Right Box. Write each spelling word in the correct box.

r-controlled o:

One Syllable	Two Syllables
1. _____	1. _____
2. _____	2. _____
3. _____	3. _____
4. _____	4. _____
	5. _____
	6. _____

Long o With e Plus an Ending:

1. _____	5. _____
2. _____	6. _____
3. _____	7. _____
4. _____	

Long o With Silent e Ending:

1. _____   2. _____

A Contraction With Long o: 1. _____

V. Drawing Conclusions. Complete each conclusion with a word from the spelling list. If you need help, use the **Glossary/SPELLEX®**.

a. Amy watered the garden. Most likely she used a _____ .

b. Senator Gray was reelected. She received the most _____ .

c. The ice cubes had hardened. No doubt they were _____ .

d. Dogs and cats are different. Dogs bark. Cats _____ .

e. I traveled solo. The trip was a _____ one.

f. Rust and tan are similar colors. They are brown _____ .

g. The camper was homesick. He was _____ for his parents.

h. The comedian caused much laughter. Perhaps he told many _____ .

i. We each ate half of the pie. The _____ pie was eaten.

j. Gail was elected class president. Gail was _____ .

16

Spelling Words

*hose   whole   jokes   tones   votes   chosen   frozen
lonely   lonesome   don't   ore   bore   border   forbid
scorn   northern   formed   ordered   orchard   forward*

IV. Compare and Contrast. Use each of the spelling words in one of the
phrases below.

a. not ballots, but _____

b. not entertain, but _____

c. not _____, but asked

d. not the center, but the _____

e. not shaped, but _____

f. not _____, but melted

g. not admire, but _____

h. not polished metal, but _____

i. not half, but _____

j. not sociable, but _____

k. not _____, but allow

l. not _____, but backward

m. not _____, but forest

n. not happy, but _____

o. not _____, but southern

p. not _____, but riddles

q. not squawks, but pleasant _____

r. not do, but _____

s. not with a sprinkler, but with a _____

t. not rejected, but _____

VII. Be a Word Detective. The same two letters are missing from each of the words below. Write the words.

Line 1		f			w	a	r	d	■		b			d	e	r
Line 2			f			b	i	d	■			e	■	s	c		n
Line 3	f			m	e	d	■			d	e	r	e	d	■	b		e
Line 4				c	h	a	r	d	■		n			t	h	e	r	n

Write the words.

Line 1 _____ _____

Line 2 _____ _____ _____

Line 3 _____ _____ _____

Line 4 _____ _____

VIII. All in a Sentence. Use each of the spelling words in sentences about one of the following titles. Use as many **Other Word Forms** (p. 15) as you can. Circle the spelling words and the other word forms you used.

<u>Gardens in Winter</u> or <u>Outdoor Recess</u>

Example: *We walked to the* (*northern*) (*orchards*).

IX. Final Test. Write each spelling word.

18

Lesson 5

I. Check Test. Write each spelling word.

II. Spelling Words and Phrases

cute	**cute** baby
amuse	to **amuse** with stories
excuse	made no **excuse**
usually	**usually** done on time
uniform	wore a **uniform**
unit	a small **unit**
pupil	one for each **pupil**
choose	will **choose** my own
stoop	had to **stoop** down low
troop	will **troop** down the hall
foolish	seemed rather **foolish**
loose	some **loose** change
spoon	stirred with a **spoon**
smooth	will **smooth** the bedspread
mood	in a bad **mood**
junior	a **junior** in college
juicy	too **juicy** for a fork
secure	will **secure** with a lock
surely	if we **surely** must
aren't	if we **aren't** ready

III. Find a Fit. Write each word in its correct shape.

a.

b.

c.

d.

e.

f.

g.

h.

i.

j.

k.

l.

m.

n.

o.

p.

q.

r.

s.

t.

Other Word Forms

cuter, cutest, amused, amusing, excuses, excused, excusing, usual, uniformly, units, unity, pupils, chose, choosing, stooped, troops, trooped, fool, foolishly, looser, loosely, loosen, spooned, smoothly, smoother, smoothness, smoothed, moody, juniors, juice, juicier, juiciest, secured, securing, sure, surer

19

IV. All in a Row. Write the twenty spelling words in alphabetical order. Then join the boxed letters and write four hidden words.

1. __ __ __ ☐ __
2. __ __ __ ☐ __ ,
3. __ __ ☐ __ __ __
4. __ ☐ ☐ __
5. __ __ __ __ ☐ __

Hidden Word: _____

6. ☐ __ __ __ __ __ __
7. __ __ ☐ __ __
8. __ __ ☐ __ __ __
9. __ __ __ __ ☐
10. __ __ __ ☐

Hidden Word: _____

11. __ __ __ __ ☐
12. __ ☐ __ __ __ __
13. __ ☐ __ __ __ __
14. __ __ ☐ __ ☐
15. ☐ __ __ __ __

Hidden Word: _____

16. ☐ __ __ __ __ __
17. ☐ __ __ __ __
18. ☐ __ __ __ __ __ __
19. __ ☐ __ ☐
20. __ ☐ __ __ __ __ __

Hidden Word: _____

V. Word Parts. Using the letters below, write the eight oo words from the spelling list.

sp sm		se p
m l f	oo	n th
tr st ch		lish d

1. _____
2. _____
3. _____
4. _____
5. _____
6. _____
7. _____
8. _____

20

Spelling Words

cute amuse excuse usually uniform unit pupil
choose stoop troop foolish loose spoon smooth
mood junior juicy secure surely aren't

VI. Crossword Puzzle. Solve the puzzle by using all the words from the spelling
list. Check your answers in the **Glossary/SPELLEX®**.

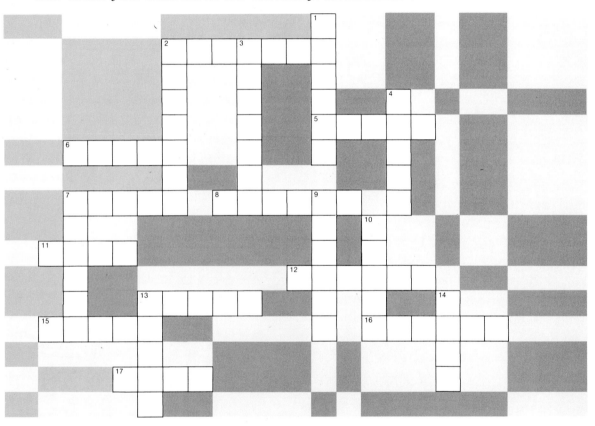

Across

2. an outfit
5. to move together in a large group
6. a student
7. watery
8. to decide or select
11. one thing
12. to fasten firmly
13. not a fork or a knife
15. are not (contraction)
16. a reason given
17. a state of mind

Down

1. to make flat
2. ordinarily
3. without sense
4. not tight
7. younger
9. certainly
10. to entertain
13. to bend down
14. pretty

21

VII. Finding Words. The words in the spelling list appear in the beginning (A-H), middle (I-Q), or end (R-Z) of the **Glossary/SPELLEX®**. Write each word.

Beginning A-H	Middle I-Q	End R-Z
1. _____	1. _____	1. _____
2. _____	2. _____	2. _____
3. _____	3. _____	3. _____
4. _____	4. _____	4. _____
5. _____	5. _____	5. _____
6. _____		6. _____
		7. _____
		8. _____
		9. _____

VIII. All in a Sentence. Use each of the spelling words in sentences about one of the following titles. Use as many **Other Word Forms** (p. 19). Circle the spelling words and the other word forms you used.

<u>The Field Trip</u> or <u>Taking a Hike</u>

Example: *Twenty (pupils) (trooped) down the path.*

IX. Final Test. Write each spelling word.

22

1	2	3	4	5
beam	dried	final	knives	ore
beaten	eastern	frozen	lonely	safely
compare	easy	grace	mood	spoon
cute	excuse	ideal	northern	tones
decide	fare	item	operate	unit

I. Hide and Seek. Twenty-five other forms of the spelling words can be found in the word puzzle. The words appear down, across, and diagonally. Find the words. Circle and write each word. Use the **Glossary/SPELLEX®**.

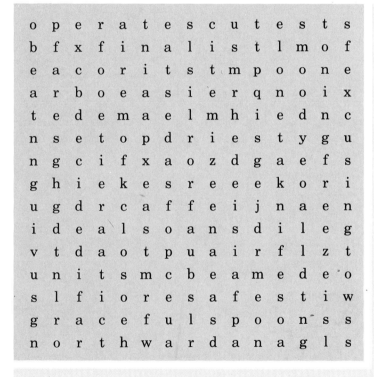

```
o p e r a t e s c u t e s t s
b f x f i n a l i s t l m o f
e a c o r i t s t m p o o n e
a r b o e a s i e r q n o i x
t e d e m a e l m h i e d n c
n s e t o p d r i e s t y g u
n g c i f x a o z d g a e f s
g h i e k e s r e e k o r i
u g d r c a f f e i j n a e n
i d e a l s o a n s d i l e g
v t d a o t p u a i r f l z t
u n i t s m c b e a m e d e o
s l f i o r e s a f e s t i w
g r a c e f u l s p o o n s s
n o r t h w a r d a n a g l s
```

Across

1.
2.
3.
4.
5.
6.
7.
8.
9.
10.
11.
12.
13.

Down

1.
2.
3.
4.
5.
6.
7.
8.
9.
10.
11.

Diagonally

1.

23

6

1	2	3	4	5
crazy	invite	cheat	heap	juicy
seal	escape	chosen	border	lively
whale	rare	tied	guide	forbid
jokes	junior	ordered	rise	smooth
greatest	foolish	pupil	meanwhile	meantime

II. Books and Authors. Write other word forms or the spelling words to complete the book titles. The number tells you in what column you can find the spelling word. Write each word or its other word form only once. Capitalize each word. Use the **Glossary/SPELLEX®**.

a. Manual for _____(3)_____ and Loosening Knots by B. A. Scout

b. Across Many _____(4)_____ by Tex S. Rangers

c. The Magic of the _____(1)_____ Houdini by Otis Appear

d. A Place for _____(2)_____ and Seniors by Hy School

e. The Mystery of the _____(1)_____ Envelope by O. Penn Upp

f. And _____(4)_____ , Time Passes By! by Howe I. Linger

g. The Noisiest and _____(5)_____ Children by Anita Rest

h. A _____(3)_____ Is Never a Winner by A. Lou Zerr

i. Tammy Twig's Zaniest and _____(1)_____ Adventures by R. U. Square

j. How _____(2)_____ We Behave! by Letts B. Quiet

k. Law and _____(3)_____ by Jay Walker

l. Famous _____(1)_____ and Other Sailing Vessels by Ima Shipp

m. How _____(5)_____ We Ride! by Iva Neucarr

n. The _____(5)_____ Planet by Astro Knotts

o. Only the Tangiest and _____(5)_____ Lemons! by Wee R. Squirts

p. The Largest and _____(2)_____ Jewel in the Crown by Ruby Rich

q. How Wild Is the _____(1)_____ ? by Decca Cards

r. Six _____(3)_____ for the School by Getta T. Chur

s. Land of the _____(4)_____ Sun by Orrie Ental

t. The Leaders Our Forefathers _____(3)_____ by U. R. King

u. The Last _____(2)_____ Dinner Guest by I. M. Hungry

v. In the _____(5)_____ , There's Work to Do! by Wee R. Lazy

w. Great _____(4)_____ Piles by Hyer and Hyer

x. The Book of Daring _____(2)_____ by U. May Runn

y. Lighthouses: Great _____(4)_____ Lights by I. C. Better

1	2	3	4	5	**6**
break	bare	scare	I'll	mistake	
peace	we're	dealing	reached	we've	
divide	hadn't	doesn't	I'd	I've	
hose	votes	formed	forward	don't	
amuse	usually	uniform	troop	aren't	

III. Calendar of Events. Use other word forms or the spelling words to write a silly or serious note for each day of a school calendar. Circle the other word forms and the spelling words you used. Two days are filled out for you.

MON	TUES	WED	THURS	FRI
		1	2	3
6	7 ⟨*formed*⟩ *a group*	8	9	10
13	14	15	16	17
20	21	22	23	24
27	28	29	30	31 ⟨*I've*⟩ *survived the month.*

6

1	2	3	4	5
graze	secure	filing	scorn	seashore
brake	preach	lonesome	stoop	ninth
square	grapes	choose	reaches	orchard
scarce	bore	really	lining	loose
preparing	reason	finest	surely	whole

IV. **Sentence Completion.** Write other word forms or the spelling words to complete the sentences. The number tells you in what column you can find the spelling word. Write each word or its other word form only once. If you need help, use the **Glossary/SPELLEX®**.

a. I _____*chose*_____ not to eat the one _____ that looked soft.
           3   2

b. The _____ in a car should be tightened _____ .
        1   2

c. Our math teacher told us the many _____ for teaching the area of
                         2

    triangles and _____ .
                1

d. Southern farmers are _____ that oranges will be _____
                4   1

    this summer because of the cold winter.

e. My dad _____ a _____ meal for us.
           1   5

f. The cow looked _____ as it _____ in the pasture.
              3   1

g. Some children were _____ when the teacher _____
              2   2

    about safety.

h. He _____ down to put the _____ into the metal cabinet.
       4   3

i. Her painting of the apple _____ looked very _____ .
                  5   3

j. The _____ yards of material was of _____ quality.
        5   3

k. My little brother _____ the idea of making straight _____
              4   4

    on his homework paper.

l. When I _____ for the _____ tied rope, the knot
        4   5

    came undone.

m. We visited many _____ on our vacation.
             5

26

Lesson 7

I. **Check Test.** Write each spelling word.

II. **Spelling Words and Phrases**

aim	took **aim**
bait	the last worm for **bait**
gain	to **gain** weight
braid	a ribbon on each **braid**
brain	controlled by the **brain**
strain	to **strain** on the rope
remain	will **remain** here
faint	will **faint** in the heat
waist	around your **waist**
sailor	the **sailor** in uniform
daily	a **daily** delivery
praise	**praise** for good work
straight	drew a **straight** line
fairly	was treated **fairly**
sway	will **sway** in the wind
spray	a **spray** of water
stray	to **stray** from course
payment	a monthly **payment**
mayor	the office of the **mayor**
delayed	**delayed** the plane

III. **Find a Fit.** Write each word in its correct shape.

a.
b.
c.
d.
e.
f.
g.
h.
i.
j.
k.
l.
m.
n.
o.
p.
q.
r.
s.
t.

Other Word Forms

aimed, aimless, baited, gained, gainful, braided, braiding, brains, brainy, strained, strainer, remains, remained, remaining, fainted, faintly, waists, sailors, day, praises, praising, straighten, straightest, straightening, fair, fairer, fairest, swaying, sprayed, strayed, pay, pays, paid, paying, mayors, delay, delays, delaying

27

IV. Patterns. Complete the words below by adding the correct *a* sound. Write the words. Each word can be found in the spelling list.

Patterns	Spelling Words	Patterns	Spelling Words
a. rem __ __ n	_____	k. spr __ __	_____
b. d __ __ ly	_____	l. s __ __ lor	_____
c. br __ __ n	_____	m. f __ __ nt	_____
d. del __ __ ed	_____	n. g __ __ n	_____
e. m __ __ or	_____	o. f __ __ rly	_____
f. sw __ __	_____	p. p __ __ ment	_____
g. pr __ __ se	_____	q. w __ __ st	_____
h. b __ __ t	_____	r. __ __ m	_____
i. str __ __ n	_____	s. str __ __ ght	_____
j. br __ __ d	_____	t. str __ __	_____

V. BrAIn Game. Answer each question with an <u>ai</u> word from the spelling list.

a. What <u>ai</u> do you use to think? _____

b. What <u>ai</u> has to do with fishing? _____

c. What <u>ai</u> leaves you behind? _____

d. What <u>ai</u> separates out the water? _____

e. What <u>ai</u> goes to sea? _____

f. What <u>ai</u> occurs when you are ill? _____

g. What <u>ai</u> is part of your body? _____

h. What <u>ai</u> is found each day? _____

i. What <u>ai</u> is what the girl did to her hair? _____

j. What <u>ai</u> do you get when you have done well? _____

k. What <u>ai</u> does not curve? _____

l. What <u>ai</u> helps you reach your goal? _____

m. What <u>ai</u> increases your weight? _____

n. What <u>ai</u> treats you honestly? _____

Write the six remaining spelling words in alphabetical order.

1. _____   3. _____   5. _____

2. _____   4. _____   6. _____

Spelling Words

*aim bait gain braid brain strain remain
faint waist sailor daily praise straight fairly
sway spray stray payment mayor delayed*

VI. Words and Meanings. Write a spelling word for each meaning. Check your
answers in the **Glossary/SPELLEX®**.

a. done every day _____

b. the body part above the hips _____

c. words that tell the worth of something _____

d. strands of hair woven together _____

e. the head of a city's government _____

f. to increase in weight _____

g. a member of a ship's crew _____

h. to move back and forth _____

i. not bent or curved _____

j. to pull hard _____

k. a moving group of water droplets _____

l. to stay in a place _____

m. to wander from the right path _____

n. an amount paid _____

o. honestly and justly _____

p. to lose consciousness for a short time _____

q. anything used to attract animals to be caught _____

r. put off until later _____

s. the part of the nervous system in the skull _____

t. a purpose or goal _____

VII. Many Meanings. Each pair of questions shows two uses of a spelling word. Use the **Glossary/SPELLEX®** to help you decide the meaning of the spelling word in each question. Write the spelling word in a sentence that answers each question.

   a. 1. What is your <u>aim</u> in school this year?

       2. What do you use to take <u>aim</u> at a bull's-eye?

   b. 1. How do you <u>strain</u> the lumps out of gravy?

       2. Do you <u>strain</u> when you pull a heavy box by a rope?

   c. 1. Can you <u>braid</u> your hair?

       2. Can you make more than one <u>braid</u> in sixty seconds?

VIII. Book List. Using all of the spelling words, make up titles and authors for books. You may use **Other Word Forms** (p. 27). Circle the spelling words and the other word forms you used.

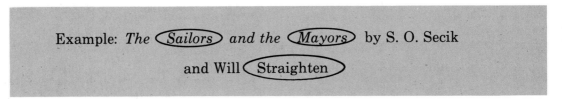

Example: *The* (Sailors) *and the* (Mayors) by S. O. Secik

and Will (Straighten)

IX. Final Test. Write each spelling word.

Lesson 8

I. Check Test. Write each spelling word.

II. Spelling Words and Phrases

deed	good **deed**
needle	knitting **needle**
creek	fish in the **creek**
sleeve	patch on my **sleeve**
freeze	began to **freeze**
freedom	enjoyed **freedom**
bleeding	stopped the **bleeding**
Halloween	**Halloween** party
piece	a **piece** of paper
chief	reported to the **chief**
view	**view** from the top
ironing	a stack of **ironing**
rifle	held the **rifle**
climate	cool, dry **climate**
excite	will **excite** the crowd
exciting	an **exciting** vacation
replied	**replied** without delay
flight	took the next **flight**
fright	recovered from our **fright**
all right	**all right** and safe

III. Find a Fit. Write each word in its correct shape.

a.
b.
c.
d.
e.
f.
g.
h.
i.
j.
k.
l.
m. Need
n.
o.
p.
q.
r.
s.
t.

Other Word Forms

deeded, needles, needled, creeks, sleeves, froze, frozen, freezer, freezes, freezing, free, freely, bleed, bled, blood, pieces, pieced, chiefs, chiefly, viewed, viewer, iron, ironed, rifles, rifled, climates, excited, reply, replies, replying, flights, frighten, frightened, frightening

IV. Word Match-ups. Find a word in the spelling list that best fits each phrase or word below. Check your answers in the **Glossary/SPELLEX®**.

a. atmosphere _____

b. removing wrinkles _____

c. supervisor _____

d. part of _____

e. small stream _____

f. sight _____

g. long weapon _____

h. OK _____

i. sewing tool _____

j. an act _____

k. a children's holiday _____

l. thrilling _____

m. fresh wound _____

n. caused by Frankenstein _____

o. stand perfectly still _____

p. a set of stairs _____

q. answered _____

r. arm covering _____

s. to thrill _____

t. liberty _____

Spelling Words

deed needle creek sleeve freeze freedom bleeding
Halloween piece chief view ironing rifle climate
excite exciting replied flight fright all right

V. Scrambled Words. Unscramble each word to find a word from the spelling list. Write the word.

a. fechi _____ k. ecipe _____

b. deplier _____ l. veslee _____

c. flier _____ m. kecre _____

d. wive _____ n. tengicix _____

e. dleene _____ o. eded _____

f. ceetix _____ p. walloneeH _____

g. riniong _____ q. zefree _____

h. dofreme _____ r. ghtifr _____

i. blengdie _____ s. lal ightr _____

j. miclate _____ t. ghtifl _____

VI. Finding Words. The words in the spelling list appear in the beginning (A-H), middle (I-Q), or end (R-Z) of the **Glossary/SPELLEX®**. Write each word.

Beginning A-H		Middle I-Q	End R-Z
1. _____	9. _____	1. _____	1. _____
2. _____	10. _____	2. _____	2. _____
3. _____	11. _____	3. _____	3. _____
4. _____	12. _____		4. _____
5. _____	13. _____		
6. _____			
7. _____			
8. _____			

VII. Rhyming Words. Choose words from the spelling list to rhyme with the words below.

a. do _____

b. beside _____

c. delighting _____

d. bead _____

e. admiring _____

f. mean _____

g. seize _____

h. niece _____

i. leaf _____

j. tweedle _____

k. believe _____

l. beak _____

m. trifle _____

n. feeding _____

o. Fahrenheit _____

_____

_____

_____

Write the two spelling words that do not have a rhyming word.

_____   _____

VIII. Write Your Journal. Use each of the spelling words or **Other Word Forms** (p. 31) to write a page in your journal about the day you went to an outdoor sporting event. Circle the spelling words and the other word forms you used.

IX. Final Test. Write each spelling word.

I. Check Test. Write each spelling word.

II. Spelling Words and Phrases

burst	to **burst** through the door
burglar	startled the **burglar**
further	**further** down the road
surprises	enjoys **surprises**
overturn	to **overturn** the boat
overcome	**overcome** with joy
forever	**forever** and a day
motor	started the **motor**
moment	at the last **moment**
program	a different **program**
protest	to **protest** the decision
odd	**odd** or even
golf	a game of **golf**
bond	their **bond** of friendship
moss	covered with **moss**
toss	began to **toss** and turn
lodge	stayed at the **lodge**
topic	chose a **topic**
crops	harvested their **crops**
stuff	will **stuff** with newspaper

III. Find a Fit. Write each word in its correct shape.

a.
b.
c.
d.
e.
f.
g.
h.
i.
j.
k.
l.
m.
n.
o.
p.
q.
r.
s.
t.

Other Word Forms
bursting, burglary, furthered, furthermore, surprised, surprising, overturned, overturning, overcame, overcoming, motorist, motoring, moments, programmed, programming, programmer, protested, protester, oddly, oddest, golfer, golfing, bonding, bondage, mossy, tossed, lodged, lodging, lodger, topics, cropped, stuffed

IV. All in a Row. Write the twenty spelling words in alphabetical order.
Then join the boxed letters and write four hidden words.

1. __ __ □ __
2. __ □ __ __ __ __
3. __ __ □ __ __
4. __ __ __ □ __
5. __ __ __ □ __ __

Hidden Word: _____

11. □ __ __ __ __
12. □ __ __
13. __ □ __ __ __ __ __
14. __ __ □ __ __ __ __
15. __ □ __ __ __ __ __

Hidden Word: _____

6. __ __ □ __ __ __ __
7. __ □ __ __
8. __ □ __ __ __
9. □ __ __ __ __ __
10. __ __ __ □

Hidden Word: _____

16. __ __ __ __ __ □ __
17. __ □ __ __ __
18. __ __ __ __ __ __ □ __
19. __ __ □ __ __
20. __ __ __ □

Hidden Word: _____

V. Hide and Seek. The spelling words can be found in the word puzzle. The words
appear across and down. Circle and write the words.

Across

1. ⬜⬜⬜⬜⬜⬜
2. ⬜⬜⬜⬜⬜⬜
3. ⬜⬜⬜
4. ⬜⬜⬜
5. ⬜⬜⬜
6. ⬜⬜⬜
7. ⬜⬜⬜⬜
8. ⬜⬜⬜⬜⬜
9. ⬜⬜⬜
10. ⬜⬜⬜⬜⬜

11. ⬜⬜⬜
12. ⬜⬜⬜⬜
13. ⬜⬜⬜

Down

1. ⬜⬜⬜
2. ⬜⬜⬜⬜
3. ⬜⬜⬜
4. ⬜⬜
5. ⬜⬜

a	b	b	g	o	f	o	r	e	v	e	r	w	s
s	u	u	o	d	o	v	e	r	t	u	r	n	u
t	r	r	l	d	d	e	l	e	m	o	t	o	r
u	g	s	f	w	c	r	o	p	s	l	o	j	p
f	l	t	o	p	i	c	k	b	o	n	d	w	r
f	a	l	j	m	m	o	m	e	n	t	m	l	i
p	r	o	g	r	a	m	o	m	l	m	o	s	s
r	f	u	r	t	h	e	r	o	l	o	d	g	e
p	r	o	t	e	s	t	r	l	o	t	o	s	s

6. ⬜⬜⬜⬜⬜⬜⬜   7. ⬜⬜⬜⬜⬜⬜⬜

Spelling Words

burst burglar further surprises overturn overcome forever motor moment program protest odd golf bond moss toss lodge topic crops stuff

VI. Words and Meanings. Write a spelling word for each meaning. Check your answers in the **Glossary/SPELLEX®**. You may wish to look up the meanings of *burst* and *toss*.

a. a length of time that never ends _____

b. something that ties or unites _____

c. a very brief space of time _____

d. made helpless _____

e. at a greater amount _____

f. a subject _____

g. to show objection to _____

h. to do suddenly or by force _____

i. not even _____

j. a person who steals _____

k. an engine _____

l. to turn upside down _____

m. things not expected _____

n. green plants that form on trees _____

o. an outdoor game played with clubs and a ball _____

p. plants grown for food _____

q. a plan of what will be done _____

r. a countrylike house _____

s. to pack too fully _____

t. to move about with force _____

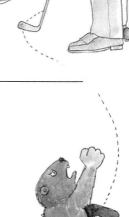

VII. Little Word—Big Word. Write the big word from the spelling list that includes each little word below.

a. You find an <u>urn</u> in _____ .   d. There is a <u>rise</u> in _____ .

b. There are <u>men</u> in a _____ .   e. You find a <u>top</u> in _____ .

c. See the <u>test</u> in _____ .

VIII. Writing Sentences. Write each set of words in a sentence about a summer weekend. You may use **Other Word Forms** (p. 35).

1. crops—odd—topic

2. motor—overturn—burst

3. surprises—further—moment

4. golf—program—forever

5. protest—bond—overcome

6. lodge—stuff—moss

7. burglar—toss

IX. Final Test. Write each spelling word.

Lesson 10

I. Check Test. Write each spelling word.

II. Spelling Words and Phrases

soak	to **soak** for ten minutes
loan	a **loan** from the bank
loafing	no time for **loafing**
unload	to **unload** the truck
foul	to hit another **foul**
trout	stocked with **trout**
crouch	to **crouch** low for the ball
blouse	tucked in the **blouse**
county	into the next **county**
mountain	a **mountain** trail
pronounce	hard to **pronounce**
howl	a **howl** of pain
scowl	an angry **scowl**
growl	a frightening **growl**
coward	scared the **coward**
crowded	across the **crowded** room
powder	crushed into **powder**
however	**however** they tried
downstairs	dashed **downstairs**
sour	**sour** milk

III. Find a Fit. Write each word in its correct shape.

a.
b.
c.
d.
e.
f.
g.
h.
i.
j.
k.
l.
m.
n.
o.
p.
q.
r.
s.
t.

Other Word Forms
soaked, loaned, loaf, loafs, loafed, loafer, unloaded, unloading, fouled, fouling, trouts, crouches, crouched, blouses, counties, mountainous, pronounces, pronounced, pronouncing, howled, howling, scowls, scowled, growled, cowards, crowd, powdered, powdering, soured, sourest

IV. Break the Code. Use the code to write the spelling words.

a	b	c	d	e	f	g	h	i	j	k	l	m
↕	↕	↕	↕	↕	↕	↕	↕	↕	↕	↕	↕	↕
z	y	x	w	v	u	t	s	r	q	p	o	n

a. gilfg _____

b. olzurmt _____

c. fmolzw _____

d. nlfmgzrm _____

e. sldo _____

f. kldwvi _____

g. ulfo _____

h. yolfhv _____

i. hlzp _____

j. tildo _____

k. xildwvw _____

l. xldziw _____

m. wldmhgzrih _____

n. hlfi _____

o. xlfmgb _____

p. olzm _____

q. kilmlfmxv _____

r. xilfxs _____

s. sldvevi _____

t. hxldo _____

V. Oh, the Pain! Find the missing letters and soothe the hurt. Write the words.

a. h __ __ ever _____

b. m __ __ ntain _____

c. gr __ __ l _____

d. f __ __ l _____

e. p __ __ der _____

f. c __ __ nty _____

g. c __ __ ard _____

h. s __ __ k _____

i. tr __ __ t _____

j. sc __ __ l _____

k. l __ __ fing _____

l. bl __ __ se _____

m. cr __ __ ch _____

n. unl __ __ d _____

o. h __ __ l _____

p. d __ __ nstairs _____

q. l __ __ n _____

r. cr __ __ ded _____

s. pron __ __ nce _____

t. s __ __ r _____

40

Spelling Words

soak loan loafing unload foul trout crouch blouse county mountain pronounce howl scowl growl coward crowded powder however downstairs sour

IV. Name the Book. Solve the puzzles and read down the column to discover the title of a classic children's book.

a. a brook fish ☐ __ __ __ __

b. snarl __ ☐ __ __ __

c. dustlike material __ __ __ __ ☐ __

d. remove a cargo __ __ __ __ ☐ __

e. not upstairs __ __ __ __ ☐ __ __ __ __

f. not a fair ball __ __ ☐ __

g. speak sounds __ ☐ __ __ __ __ __ __ __

h. a woman's shirt __ __ __ __ __ ☐

i. idling __ __ __ __ ☐ __ __

j. place in water ☐ __ __ __

k. money borrowed ☐ __ __ __

l. a steep hill __ __ __ __ __ ☐ __

m. not a state __ __ __ ☐ __ __

n. not a hero __ __ __ __ __ ☐

The name of the book is: _____   _____

VII. Finding Words. The words in the spelling list appear in the beginning (A-H), middle (I-Q), or end (R-Z) of the **Glossary/SPELLEX®**. Write each word.

Beginning A-H	Middle I-Q	End R-Z
1. _____	1. _____	1. _____
2. _____	2. _____	2. _____
3. _____	3. _____	3. _____
4. _____	4. _____	4. _____
5. _____	5. _____	5. _____
6. _____		
7. _____		
8. _____		
9. _____		
10. _____		

VIII. Book List. Using all of the spelling words, make up titles and authors for books. You may use **Other Word Forms** (p. 39). Circle the spelling words and the other word forms you used.

IX. Final Test. Write each spelling word.

Lesson 11

I. Check Test. Write each spelling word.

II. Spelling Words and Phrases

sentence	the verb in the **sentence**
depend	to **depend** on others
invent	to **invent** the wheel
intend	**intend** to travel
intent	to know their **intent**
empty	the **empty** house
helmet	a motorcycle **helmet**
herd	a **herd** of elephants
clerk	the store **clerk**
person	a friendly **person**
perhaps	will do it later **perhaps**
merchant	supplied by a **merchant**
perfume	the smell of **perfume**
weren't	if you **weren't** certain
American	the **American** flag
desert	a trip across the **desert**
member	greeted the new **member**
temper	in control of my **temper**
general	the **general** idea
entered	**entered** the room

III. Find a Fit. Write each word in its correct shape.

a.
b.
c.
d.
e.
f.
g.
h.
i.
j.
k.
l.
m.
n.
o.
p.
q.
r.
s.
t.

Other Word Forms

sentenced, sentencing, depended, dependable, dependent, invented, inventor, intended, intention, intentional, emptied, emptying, helmets, herded, herding, clerking, clerical, personal, personally, personality, personable, merchandise, perfumed, America, deserted, deserting, deserter, membership, tempered, generally, generality, enter, entering

43

IV. Crossword Puzzle. Solve the puzzle by using all the words from the spelling list. Check your answers in the **Glossary/SPELLEX®**.

Across

1. a citizen of the U.S.
4. an army officer
5. to plan or to mean
8. a protective hat
9. a human being
10. purpose
13. a salesperson
14. came in
16. one of a group
17. to rely
18. not full

Down

2. one who sells
3. a group of cows
6. one's mood
7. were not (contraction)
9. a sweet-smelling liquid
10. to create something new
11. has a subject and predicate
12. maybe
15. a dry region

44

Spelling Words

*sentence depend invent intend intent empty helmet
herd clerk person perhaps merchant perfume weren't
American desert member temper general entered*

V. Compare and Contrast. Use each of the spelling words in one of the phrases below.

a. not a phrase, but a _____

b. not an outsider, but a _____

c. not _____ , but exited

d. not specific, but _____

e. not a _____ , but a swamp

f. not a _____ , but a hat

g. not copy, but _____

h. not full, but _____

i. not a buyer, but a _____

j. not a flock, but a _____

k. not _____ , but English

l. not were, but _____

m. not a manager, but a _____

n. not an animal, but a _____

o. not _____ , but definitely

p. not an _____ , but a purpose

q. not a skunk smell, but _____

r. not _____ , but do not plan to

s. not to distrust, but to _____ on

t. not calm and peaceful, but with a _____

VI. All in a Row. Write the twenty spelling words in alphabetical order. Then join the boxed letters and write four hidden words.

1. __ __ __ __ __ __ __ □
2. __ __ □ __ __ __
3. __ __ __ □ __ __
4. □ __ __ __ __
5. __ __ __ __ □

Hidden Word: _____

11. __ __ __ __ □ __ __
12. □ __ __ □ __ __
13. □ __ __ □ __ __
14. __ __ □ __ __ __ __
15. __ __ □ __ __ __

Hidden Word: _____

6. __ □ __ __ __ __
7. __ __ __ __ □ __
8. __ __ __ □ __ __
9. __ □ __ __
10. __ __ __ __ □

Hidden Word: _____

16. __ __ __ __ __ __ □
17. __ __ __ __ □ __
18. __ □ __ __ __ __ __
19. __ __ __ □ __ ,
20. __ __ □ __ __ ' __

Hidden Word: _____

VII. Poetry Corner. Using **Other Word Forms** (p. 43), make up titles for poems. Circle the other word forms.

Example: (Herds) and Flocks

VIII. Final Test. Write each spelling word.

1	2	3	4	5
bait	depend	helmet	moment	replied
bond	desert	however	mountain	scowl
chief	freedom	invent	odd	strain
county	freeze	member	powder	topic
delayed	fright	merchant	pronounce	trout

I. Break the Code. Use the code to write spelling words or other word forms. Write each word.

a	b	c	d	e	f	g	h	i	j	k	l	m	n	o	p	q	r	s	t	u	v	w	x	y	z
↓	↓	↓	↓	↓	↓	↓	↓	↓	↓	↓	↓	↓	↓	↓	↓	↓	↓	↓	↓	↓	↓	↓	↓	↓	↓
g	d	j	r	u	e	y	w	k	a	c	p	s	h	b	n	l	m	f	o	t	x	z	v	q	i

a. tbbqg

b. sdtwfp

c. otpbm

d. utlzkm

e. knzfsm

f. dflqzfm

g. rtrfpum

h. sdffqg

i. ojzuzpa

j. bfmfdum

k. nfqrfum

l. udteu

m. nthfxfd

n. bflfpbzpa

o. zpxfputd

p. sdzanufpfb

q. ktepuzfm

r. mudjzpfd

s. bfqjgzpa

t. lthbfdfb

u. mkthqzpa

v. ldtpepkzjuztp

w. rfrofdmnzl

x. rtepujzptem

y. rfdknjpum

47

12

1	2	3	4	5
American	downstairs	ironing	perfume	spray
blouse	empty	loafing	perhaps	straight
burglar	excite	needle	protest	surprises
coward	forever	overcome	sailor	temper
deed	golf	payment	sentence	weren't

II. Hide and Seek.
Twenty-one other word forms and four spelling words can be found in the word puzzle. The words appear across and down. Circle and write the words. Capitalize the other form of *American*. Use the **Glossary/SPELLEX®**.

Across

1.
2.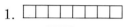
3.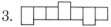
4.
5.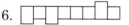
6.
7.
8.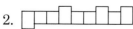
9.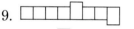
10.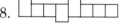
11.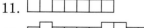
12.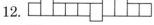
13.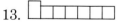

```
i  o  v  e  r  c  a  m  e  d  e  w  s  d  a
r  o  e  s  g  o  l  f  e  r  n  e  u  o  m
o  t  i  p  e  r  h  a  p  s  t  r  r  w  e
n  x  t  e  m  p  e  r  s  p  p  e  p  n  r
s  y  z  r  w  s  l  n  s  r  s  n  r  s  i
l  o  a  f  e  r  t  t  a  a  n  t  i  t  c
f  o  m  u  o  s  h  o  i  y  e  c  s  a  a
p  a  y  m  e  n  t  s  l  i  e  o  e  i  l
r  d  d  e  e  d  s  w  o  n  d  w  d  r  m
o  n  d  s  l  e  b  u  r  g  l  a  r  s  e
t  c  m  o  r  i  u  a  s  f  e  r  m  i  m
e  x  c  i  t  i  n  g  o  r  s  d  r  u  p
s  e  n  t  e  n  c  i  n  g  g  l  o  u  t
t  o  b  l  o  u  s  e  s  t  o  y  e  r  i
e  n  r  e  s  t  r  a  i  g  h  t  e  n  e
d  f  o  r  e  v  e  r  p  r  o  t  h  s  s
```

Down

1.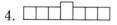
2.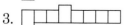
3.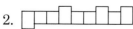
4.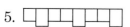
5.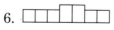

6.
7.
8.
9.

10.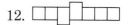
11.
12.

48

1	2	3	4	5
faint	praise	remain	aim	gain
sleeve	piece	flight	rifle	mayor
further	overturn	motor	program	moss
foul	loan	unload	all right	crouch
Halloween	intent	intend	general	entered

III. Word Building.

a. Seventeen spelling words have an *ing* form. Write the seventeen spelling words and their *ing* forms. If you need help, use the **Glossary/SPELLEX®**.

	Spelling Word	*ing* Form		Spelling Word	*ing* Form
1.	faint	fainting	10.		
2.			11.		
3.			12.		
4.			13.		
5.			14.		
6.			15.		
7.			16.		
8.			17.		
9.					

b. Six spelling words not used above have an *s* or *es* form. Write the six spelling words and their *s* or *es* forms. If you need help, use the **Glossary/SPELLEX®**.

	Spelling Word	*s* or *es* Form		Spelling Word	*s* or *es* Form
1.			4.		
2.			5.		
3.			6.		

c. The two remaining spelling words have no other word forms. Write the two words. _____   _____

12

1	2	3	4	5
braid	brain	sway	fairly	stray
waist	climate	exciting	view	bleeding
burst	lodge	crops	stuff	toss
growl	howl	soak	sour	crowded
clerk	herd	person	daily	creek

IV. Not So Tall Tales. Write other word forms or the spelling words to complete the sentences. The number tells you in what column you can find the spelling word. Write each word or its other word form only once. If you need help, use the **Glossary/SPELLEX®**.

The Howling Clerks

At a supermarket in a cold (a.) _____ (2) , two grocery (b.) _____ (1) often (c.) _____ (2) loudly when the (d.) _____ (5) entered. Each day was exciting for these two (e.) _____ (3) . Somehow it seemed that their (f.) _____ (2) were (g.) _____ (1) with mischief. How their (h.) _____ (5) boiled! Some days they were seen (i.) _____ (3) back and forth and (j.) _____ (1) at the (k.) _____ (2) of people who shopped. Most shoppers lived in ski (l.) _____ (2) near the (m.) _____ (5) that ran by the store. They put up with the madness (n.) _____ (4) because the clerks' work was always well done. With aprons around their (o.) _____ (1) , the clerks (p.) _____ (5) the salad for the deli, (q.) _____ (3) the dirt from the (r.) _____ (3) of lettuce, (s.) _____ (4) the turkeys for cooking, (t.) _____ (1) the bread dough into designs, and sliced the (u.) _____ (4) pickles into fancy shapes. They were always (v.) _____ (3) about their work and seldom (w.) _____ (5) from the work area. The manager (x.) _____ (4) them (y.) _____ (4) , but he kept them out of sight as much as possible.

50

Lesson 13

I. Check Test. Write each spelling word.

II. Spelling Words and Phrases

risk	to take a **risk**
limb	a sawed-off tree **limb**
limp	walked with a **limp**
skim	to **skim** these pages
split	did a **split**
strip	a short **strip** of tape
slipped	**slipped** and fell
swimming	**swimming** to the raft
skinned	**skinned** your elbow
beginning	**beginning** to rain
wicked	the **wicked** witch
quickly	moved away **quickly**
wrist	twisted my **wrist**
ditch	to dig a **ditch**
kitchen	opened the **kitchen** window
pitcher	the baseball **pitcher**
fifth	a **fifth** of the class
fifteenth	the **fifteenth** of the month
printing	writing rather than **printing**
prince	turned into a **prince**

III. Find a Fit. Write each word in its correct shape.

a.
b.
c.
d.
e.
f.
g.
h.
i.
j.
k.
l.
m.
n.
o.
p.
q.
r.
s.
t.

Other Word Forms

risky, risked, limbs, limber, limps, limped, skimmed, skimming, skimmer, splitting, stripped, stripping, slip, slips, slipping, slipper, swim, swam, swum, swimmer, skin, skinning, begin, begins, began, begun, wickedly, quick, quicker, quickest, wrists, ditches, ditched, kitchens, pitchers, five, fifteen, print, printed, printer, princes, princely

51

IV. Word Changes.

a. Add *ed* to each of the following words. Circle the new word if you had to double the final consonant.

1. risk _____   5. skin _____

2. skim _____   6. limp _____

3. ditch _____   7. strip _____

4. slip _____

b. Write the plural forms of these words. Do the plurals that end in *es* gain a syllable? _____

1. limb _____   4. ditch _____

2. wrist _____   5. pitcher _____

3. prince _____   6. kitchen _____

c. Write the ten words below. Circle the words that have double consonants. Then write the base word for each word. Use the **Glossary/SPELLEX**®.

1. slipped _____   6. quickly _____

2. wickedly _____   7. fifth _____

3. skinned _____   8. splitting _____

4. fifteenth _____   9. printing _____

5. beginning _____   10. swimming _____

Spelling Words

risk limb limp skim split strip slipped swimming skinned beginning wicked quickly wrist ditch kitchen pitcher fifth fifteenth printing prince

V. Scrambled Words.

a. Unscramble each word to find a word from the spelling list. Write the word.

1. ngiimmsw _____
2. tispl _____
3. pistr _____
4. pidslpe _____
5. nggeiinbn _____

6. retchpi _____
7. tchid _____
8. niskend _____
9. misk _____
10. inktche _____

b. Unscramble the scrambled word to find the spelling word that completes the sentence. Write the word.

Scrambled Words

1. The injured man walked with a _____ . mpli
2. Chris is in _____ grade. thiff
3. _____ actions should be avoided. deckwi
4. The _____ is heir to the throne. inprec
5. The watch is on your _____ . stiwr
6. Move _____ to avoid injury. lckyqui
7. Daredevils _____ their lives. skir
8. Marta celebrated her _____ birthday. theneffit
9. The tree _____ cracked during the storm. mbli
10. Gutenberg invented the _____ press. ntprngii

53

VI. Be a Word Doctor. Write the one operation you must perform before adding *ing* to each word. Write the new word.

Operations   **New Words**

Example: skip   _double the_ p   + ing =   _skipping_

a. slip   _____ + ing = _____

b. skim   _____ + ing = _____

c. swim   _____ + ing = _____

d. begin   _____ + ing = _____

e. skin   _____ + ing = _____

f. split   _____ + ing = _____

VII. All in a Sentence. Write all of the spelling words in sentences. Use as many **Other Word Forms** (p. 51) as you can. Circle the spelling words and the other word forms you used.

VIII. Final Test. Write each spelling word.

Lesson 14

I. Check Test. Write each spelling word.

II. Spelling Words and Phrases

model	building a **model** plane
bodies	large **bodies** of water
copies	made two **copies**
problem	solved the **problem**
offer	an **offer** to help
copper	gold and **copper**
dropped	**dropped** the dish
shopping	the plastic **shopping** bag
dollar	cost one **dollar**
collar	turned-up **collar**
bottom	the top and the **bottom**
blossom	a **blossom** on the tree
cloth	a cotton **cloth**
toward	walked **toward** the shore
quart	a **quart** of milk
quarter	a **quarter** and a dime
court	went to **court**
course	changed their **course**
balloon	blew up the **balloon**
shovel	a **shovel** and a rake

III. Find a Fit. Write each word in its correct shape.

a.
b.
c.
d.
e.
f.
g.
h.
i.
j.
k.
l.
m.
n.
o.
p.
q.
r.
s.
t.

Other Word Forms

models, modeled, body, copy, copied, copying, copier, problems, offers, offered, offering, coppery, drop, drops, dropping, dropper, shop, shopped, shops, shopper, dollars, collared, bottomless, blossoms, blossomed, cloths, clothing, clothes, towards, quarts, quartered, quartering, courted, courses, coursed, balloons, shoveled

IV. **Break the Code.** Use the code to write the spelling words.

a	b	c	d	e	f	g	h	i	j	k	l	m	n	o	p	q	r	s	t	u	v	w	x	y	z
↓	↓	↓	↓	↓	↓	↓	↓	↓	↓	↓	↓	↓	↓	↓	↓	↓	↓	↓	↓	↓	↓	↓	↓	↓	↓
c	d	a	b	g	h	e	f	k	l	i	j	o	p	m	n	s	t	q	r	w	x	u	v	z	y

a. rmuctb _____

b. swctr _____

c. swctrgt _____

d. dcjjmmp _____

e. amwtqg _____

f. amwtr _____

g. amnngt _____

h. mhhgt _____

i. djmqqmo _____

j. ntmdjgo _____

k. dmrrmo _____

l. amjjct _____

m. bmjjct _____

n. ombgj _____

o. qfmxgj _____

p. amnkgq _____

q. btmnngb _____

r. qfmnnkpe _____

s. ajmrf _____

t. dmbkgq _____

V. **Generally Speaking.** Write a spelling word in the group it best fits.

a. pint, _____ , gallon

b. fabric, material, _____

c. hoe, rake, _____

d. closer, nearer, _____

e. nickel, dime, _____

f. crime, trial, _____

g. copy, pattern, _____

h. trouble, difficulty, _____

VI. **Be a Word Doctor.** Write the one operation you must perform before adding the suffix to each word. Write the new word.

Operations		New Words
Example: swim _double the_ m	+ ing =	_swimming_
a. body _____	+ es =	_____
b. copy _____	+ es =	_____
c. shop _____	+ ing =	_____
d. drop _____	+ ed =	_____

Spelling Words

model bodies copies problem offer copper dropped
shopping dollar collar bottom blossom cloth toward
quart quarter court course balloon shovel

VII. Words and Meanings. Write a spelling word for each meaning. Check your answers in the **Glossary/SPELLEX®**. You may wish to look up the meanings of *course, offer,* and *toward*.

a. a math question to be solved _____

b. in the direction of _____

c. let fall _____

d. material made by weaving fibers together _____

e. a band of clothing around the neck _____

f. one fourth of a gallon _____

g. a small-scale copy _____

h. a rubber bag to be filled with air _____

i. a tool for lifting snow _____

j. masses of matter _____

k. the direction taken _____

l. buying things in a store _____

m. the lowest part _____

n. things made just like others _____

o. a reddish-brown element _____

p. a place where legal cases are decided _____

q. 100 cents _____

r. a suggestion or plan _____

s. 25 cents _____

t. a flower _____

VIII. Double Your Trouble. Write the spelling words that fit the patterns below. Each word has a double consonant.

Line 1	o			e	r	■	c	o			e	r	
Line 2	b	a			o	o	n	■	c	o		a	r
Line 3	d	o		a	r	■	b	o		o	m		
Line 4	b	l	o		o	m	■	d	r	o		e	d

Write the words.

Line 1 _____   _____

Line 2 _____   _____

Line 3 _____   _____

Line 4 _____   _____

IX. Writing Sentences. Write each set of words in a sentence. You may use **Other Word Forms** (p. 55).

1. quarter—copper—dollar

2. balloon—dropped—course

3. shopping—collar—cloth

4. bottom—shovel—court

5. bodies—copies—model

6. offer—toward—problem

7. quart—blossom

X. Final Test. Write each spelling word.

58

Lesson 15

I. Check Test. Write each spelling word.

II. Spelling Words and Phrases

touch	too hot to **touch**
cousin	wrote to my **cousin**
southern	the **southern** route
double	rode **double** on the sled
trouble	asking for **trouble**
rough	a **rough** surface
enough	not **enough** for three
dozen	a **dozen** yellow roses
govern	will **govern** the nation
blood	several drops of **blood**
flood	**flood** in the cellar
product	the best-selling **product**
brook	trout in the **brook**
shook	**shook** them fiercely
goodness	my **goodness**
couldn't	**couldn't** swim
wouldn't	if they **wouldn't** wait
outline	traced an **outline**
household	for **household** use only
fountain	brightly lighted **fountain**

III. Find a Fit. Write each word in its correct shape.

a.
b.
c.
d.
e.
f.
g.
h.
i.
j.
k.
l.
m.
n.
o.
p.
q.
r.
s.
t.

Other Word Forms

touches, touched, cousins, south, southerly, doubled, doubles, doubling, doubly, troubles, troubling, troubled, rougher, roughest, roughly, dozens, governing, government, bloody, bleed, bled, bleeding, floods, flooded, products, production, brooks, shake, shakes, shaking, shaky, good, outlines, outlined, outlining, households, fountains

IV. Look Out!

a. Answer each question with an <u>ou</u> word from the spelling list.

1. What <u>ou</u> is twice as much? _____

2. What <u>ou</u> shows the edge? _____

3. What <u>ou</u> was not able to? _____

4. What <u>ou</u> didn't want to? _____

5. What <u>ou</u> sprays toward the sky? _____

6. What <u>ou</u> causes problems? _____

7. What <u>ou</u> is a relative? _____

8. What <u>ou</u> is done by feeling? _____

9. What <u>ou</u> is opposite of northern? _____

10. What <u>ou</u> is found where you live? _____

11. What <u>ou</u> is as much as needed? _____

12. What <u>ou</u> is not smooth? _____

b. Answer each question with an <u>oo</u> word from the spelling list.

1. What <u>oo</u> did you do when you were frightened? _____

2. What <u>oo</u> is red in color? _____

3. What <u>oo</u> is like a stream? _____

4. What <u>oo</u> can bring great damage? _____

5. What <u>oo</u> shows kindness? _____

c. Use the three remaining spelling words or their **Other Word Forms** (p. 59) in sentences.

60

Spelling Words

touch cousin southern double trouble rough enough dozen govern blood flood product brook shook goodness couldn't wouldn't outline household fountain

V. Guide Words. These word pairs are guide words from the **Glossary/SPELLEX®**. Write the words from the spelling list that appear on the same page as each pair of guide words.

Example:

act—apartment
aim
ankle

balloon—bottom
1. _____

bought—canyon
2. _____

copy—daughter
3. _____
4. _____

day—dropped
5. _____
6. _____

dry—escape
7. _____

fifteen—freedom
8. _____
9. _____

freeze—graze
10. _____
11. _____

help—ironing
12. _____

often—pasture
13. _____

president—quart
14. _____

reply—scarf
15. _____

schoolmate—skinned
16. _____

skirt—strain
17. _____

taught—ugly
18. _____
19. _____

western—wrist
20. _____

VI. Break the Code. Use the code to write the spelling words.

a	b	c	d	e	f	g	h	i	j	k	l	m
↕	↕	↕	↕	↕	↕	↕	↕	↕	↕	↕	↕	↕
n	o	p	q	r	s	t	u	v	w	x	y	z

a. rabhtu _____

b. qbhoyr _____

c. ubhfrubyq _____

d. qbmra _____

e. oybbq _____

f. bhgyvar _____

g. gbhpu _____

h. oebbx _____

i. tbirea _____

j. sybbq _____

k. ebhtu _____

l. gebhoyr _____

m. pbhfva _____

n. fbhgurea _____

o. sbhagnva _____

p. tbbqarff _____

q. fubbx _____

r. pbhyqag _____

s. jbhyqag _____

t. cebqhpg _____

VII. Book List. Using all of the spelling words, make up titles and authors for books. You may use **Other Word Forms** (p. 59). Circle the spelling words and the other word forms you used.

VIII. Final Test. Write each spelling word.

62

Lesson 16

I. Check Test. Write each spelling word.

II. Spelling Words and Phrases

acts	two **acts** in the play
angle	a wide **angle**
ankle	a broken **ankle**
rank	the **rank** of lieutenant
thankful	**thankful** to be here
fact	as a matter of **fact**
grasp	a tight **grasp**
brass	made of **brass**
canyon	a deep, narrow **canyon**
sample	a **sample** of their work
shack	build their own **shack**
stack	tall **stack** of books
jacket	a wool **jacket**
racket	wooden tennis **racket**
hatch	a **hatch** of chicks
patch	**patch** of blue sky
catcher	**catcher** and batter
matches	book of **matches**
branches	several tree **branches**
hasn't	**hasn't** arrived yet

III. Find a Fit. Write each word in its correct shape.

a.
b.
c.
d.
e.
f.
g.
h.
i.
j.
k.
l.
m.
n.
o.
p.
q.
r.
s.
t.

Other Word Forms

act, acted, action, angles, ankles, ranks, ranked, thankfully, facts, factual, factually, grasps, brasses, brassy, canyons, samples, shacks, stacks, stacked, stacking, jackets, rackets, hatches, hatched, patches, patched, patching, catch, catches, catching, caught, catchers, match, matched, matching, branch, branched

IV. Whose Serve?

a. Write the fifteen singular nouns found on the spelling list. Then write their plural forms. Write the three plural nouns found on the spelling list. Then write their singular forms.

Singular	Plural
1. _angle_	_____
2. _____	_____
3. _____	_____
4. _____	_____
5. _____	_____
6. _____	_____
7. _____	_____
8. _____	_____
9. _____	_____
10. _____	_____
11. _____	_____
12. _____	_____
13. _____	_____
14. _____	_____
15. _____	_____
16. _____	_acts_
17. _____	_____
18. _____	_____

b. The plurals are formed by adding _____ or _____ .

Another syllable is added when the plural ends with _____ .

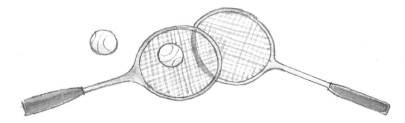

64

Spelling Words

acts angle ankle rank thankful fact grasp
brass canyon sample shack stack jacket racket
hatch patch catcher matches branches hasn't

V. All in a Row. Write the twenty spelling words in alphabetical order. Then join the boxed letters and write four hidden words.

1. __ ☐ __ __
2. __ __ __ ☐ __
3. __ __ __ __ ☐
4. __ __ ☐ __ __ __ __ __
5. __ ☐ __ __ __ __

Hidden Word: _____

6. ☐ __ __ __ __ __
7. __ __ __ __ ☐ __
8. __ ☐ __ __ __
9. __ ☐ __ __
10. __ __ __ __ ' ☐

Hidden Word: _____

11. __ *jacket* __
12. __ *matches* ☐
13. __ __ ☐ __ __ __ __
14. __ ☐ __ ☐ __ __
15. __ __ __ ☐ __ __

Hidden Word: _____

16. ☐ __ __ __
17. __ __ __ __ __ ☐
18. __ __ ☐ __ __
19. __ __ __ ☐ __
20. ☐ __ __ __ __ __ __ __

Hidden Word: _____

VI. Word Building. Add a word part to each word to build words from the spelling list. Write the words.

	s	et	es	er	ful	n't

a. jack _____
b. act _____
c. match _____
d. rack _____

e. has _____
f. catch _____
g. branch _____
h. thank _____

VII. Crossword Puzzle. Solve the puzzle by using all the words from the spelling list. Check your answers in the **Glossary/SPELLEX®**.

Across
3. a short coat
5. a pile
7. the joint near the foot
9. a true piece of information
11. to repair with cloth
12. tree limbs
15. a landform cut by a river
17. copper and zinc
19. to come out of an egg
20. an example

Down
1. used for tennis
2. a position or title
4. has not (contraction)
6. parts of a play
8. fire starters
10. grateful
13. the player behind home plate
14. a hold
16. where two lines meet
18. a small cabin

VIII. Final Test. Write each spelling word.

66

Lesson 17

I. Check Test. Write each spelling word.

II. Spelling Words and Phrases

August	an **August** thunderstorm
audience	a noisy **audience**
autumn	colorful **autumn** leaves
automobile	inspected the **automobile**
caused	has **caused** an accident
caught	**caught** a cold
taught	**taught** social studies
daughter	the oldest **daughter**
naughty	a **naughty** thing to do
astronaut	first **astronaut** on the moon
aunt	my **aunt** and uncle
often	as **often** as possible
honest	an **honest** person
holiday	summer **holiday**
knock	a **knock** on the door
control	lost **control** of the surfboard
consent	asked for **consent**
content	was **content** to wait
conduct	will **conduct** the orchestra
contract	signed the **contract**

III. Find a Fit. Write each word in its correct shape.

a.
b.
c.
d.
e.
f.
g.
h.
i.
j.
k.
l.
m.
n.
o.
p.
q.
r.
s.
t.

Other Word Forms

Aug., audiences, autumns, autumnal, automobiles, cause, causes, causing, catch, catcher, catches, catching, teach, teaches, teaching, teacher, daughters, naughtier, naughtiest, astronauts, aunts, oftener, honestly, honesty, holidays, knocks, knocked, knocking, controls, controlled, consents, consented, consenting, contents, contented, conducts, conducting, conductor, contracts

IV. Sort Your Words. Divide the spelling words into two alphabetical lists under the correct headings. Two words go in both lists.

Words Spelled With *o*

1. _____
2. _____
3. _____
4. _____
5. _____
6. _____
7. _____
8. _____
9. _____
10. _____
11. _____

Words Spelled With *au*

1. _____
2. _____
3. _____
4. _____
5. _____
6. _____
7. _____
8. _____
9. _____
10. _____
11. _____

V. Knock Down. As you knock down each bottle, unscramble the letters and write the spelling word. Then write an **Other Word Form** (p. 67) beside it.

a. ntensco
b. ntecont
c. stoneh
d. traconct
e. lotrnco
f. ckokn
g. ntua

h. dasecu
i. hayidol
j. mnuuta
k. nuctodc
l. nefto
m. ghtuac
n. taunstrao

a. _____ _____   h. _____ _____
b. _____ _____   i. _____ _____
c. _____ _____   j. _____ _____
d. _____ _____   k. _____ _____
e. _____ _____   l. _____ _____
f. _____ _____   m. _____ _____
g. _____ _____   n. _____ _____

Spelling Words

August audience autumn automobile caused caught taught daughter naughty astronaut aunt often honest holiday knock control consent content conduct contract

VI. Generally Speaking. Write each spelling word in the group it best fits.

a. vehicle, car, _____

b. seized, trapped, _____

c. tap, rap, _____

d. youngster, girl, _____

e. rest, vacation, _____

f. pleased, happy, _____

g. agreement, document, _____

h. lead, organize, _____

i. brought about, made happen, _____

j. power, command, _____

k. June, July, _____

l. instructed, informed, _____

m. OK, agree, _____

n. cousin, uncle, _____

o. crew member, pilot, _____

p. spring, summer, _____

q. frequently, usually, _____

r. truthful, fair, _____

s. bad, mean, _____

t. listeners, viewers, _____

VII. Word Detective. The same two letters are missing from each of the words below. Write the words.

a. t ___ ___ ght   _____

b. ___ ___ dience   _____

c. d ___ ___ ghter   _____

d. ___ ___ tomobile   _____

e. n ___ ___ ghty   _____

f. ___ ___ gust   _____

g. astron ___ ___ t   _____

VIII. Many Meanings. Each pair of questions shows two uses of a spelling word. Use the **Glossary/SPELLEX®** to help you decide the meaning of the spelling word in each question. Write the spelling word in a sentence that answers each question.

a. 1. Whose <u>consent</u> do you get before going to the movies?

    2. Will you <u>consent</u> to play basketball every day?

b. 1. Who can <u>conduct</u> an orchestra?

    2. Who will <u>conduct</u> your next math lesson?

c. 1. Have you <u>caught</u> a cold yet this season?

    2. Have the police <u>caught</u> a thief this past month?

IX. Final Test. Write each spelling word.

1	2	3	4	5
swimming	beginning	quickly	split	skinned
shopping	dropped	shovel	blossom	quarter
outline	trouble	southern	couldn't	wouldn't
branches	brass	grasp	matches	hasn't
automobile	knock	astronaut	holiday	August

I. Calendar of Events. Use other word forms or the spelling words to write a silly or serious note for each day of a school calendar. Circle the other word forms and the spelling words you used. Two days are filled out for you.

MON	TUES	WED	THURS	FRI
		1	2 (Drop) off letters at the post office.	3
6	7	8	9	10
13	14	15	16	17 (Begin) my report.
20	21	22	23	24
27	28	29	30	31

18

1	2	3	4	5
wicked	printing	prince	pitcher	kitchen
problem	quart	dollar	bottom	copper
product	govern	dozen	cousin	household
thankful	fact	catcher	acts	jacket
control	conduct	honest	contract	content

II. Word Building. Add word parts to each spelling word or its base word to make other word forms. If you need help, use the **Glossary/SPELLEX®**.

Spelling Words	s or es	ed	ing
Example: playing	*plays*	*played*	
a. problem	_____		
b. product	_____		
c. printing	_____	_____	
d. control	_____	_____	_____
e. fact	_____		
f. govern	_____	_____	_____
g. quart	_____		
h. dozen	_____		
i. cousin	_____		
j. content	_____	_____	
k. contract	_____	_____	_____
l. jacket	_____		
m. kitchen	_____		
n. household	_____		
o. acts		_____	_____
p. dollar	_____		
q. catcher	_____		_____
r. bottom	_____		
s. pitcher	_____	_____	_____
t. conduct	_____	_____	_____

Add word parts to each spelling word to make other word forms.

Spelling Words	ly	y
u. wicked	_____	
v. honest	_____	_____
w. thankful	_____	
x. copper		_____
y. prince	_____	

1	2	3	4	5	**18**
risk	ditch	slipped	strip	wrist	
court	collar	offer	course	toward	
shook	rough	flood	brook	fountain	
rank	shack	ankle	racket	canyon	
consent	aunt	audience	naughty	caused	

III. Raising Questions. Complete each question by writing other word forms or the spelling words. The number tells you in what column you can find the spelling word. Use each word or its other word form only once. If you need help, use the **Glossary/SPELLEX®**.

a. Were the players holding tennis _____ when they
4
_____ and fell on the ice?
3

b. Did your uncles and _____ walk _____ the shore?
2   5

c. Why are you _____ broken _____ and
1   3
_____ ?
5

d. Is the water _____ the _____ ?
3   2

e. Were the _____ _____ built?
2   2

f. Why do the _____ children _____ so many problems?
4   5

g. Has the tailor _____ the _____ from the coats?
4   2

h. Have most _____ _____ the play a success?
3   1

i. Are the _____ _____ more help to people?
1   3

j. Can nature's _____ be found in most _____ ?
5   5

k. How many golf _____ include small _____ and
4   4
streams near the greens?

l. Did you _____ his hand until he _____ to join
1   1
the club?

73

18

1	2	3	4	5
angle	caught	enough	limb	sample
autumn	cloth	fifteenth	limp	skim
balloon	copies	fifth	model	stack
blood	daughter	goodness	often	taught
bodies	double	hatch	patch	touch

IV. Before and After.

a. Find the spelling word that comes alphabetically right *before* each word below. Write the spelling word and an other word form for all but one spelling word. If you need help, use the **Glossary/SPELLEX®**.

Before	Spelling Words	Other Word Forms
1. headquarters	h a t c h	_____
2. cause	__ __ __ __ __ __	_____
3. downstairs	__ __ __ __ __ __	_____
4. day	__ __ __ __ __ __ __ __	_____
5. enter	__ __ __ __ __ __	_____
6. limp	__ __ __ __	_____
7. fifth	__ __ __ __ __ __ __ __ __	_____
8. pay	__ __ __ __ __	_____ _____
9. teach	__ __ __ __ __ __	_____
10. moment	__ __ __ __ __	_____
11. body	__ __ __ __ __	_____
12. stalk	__ __ __ __ __	_____

b. Now find the spelling word that comes alphabetically right *after* each word below. Write the spelling word and an other word form for each spelling word.

After	Spelling Words	Other Word Forms
1. automobile	__ __ __ __ __ __	_____
2. silly	__ __ __ __	_____
3. control	__ __ __ __ __ __	_____
4. closet	__ __ __ __ __	_____
5. fifteenth	__ __ __ __ __	_____
6. toss	__ __ __ __ __	_____
7. salty	__ __ __ __ __ __	_____
8. offer	__ __ __ __ __	_____
9. good	__ __ __ __ __ __ __ __	_____
10. bait	__ __ __ __ __ __ __	_____
11. limb	__ __ __ __	_____
12. blew	__ __ __ __ __	_____
13. anger	__ __ __ __ __	_____

Lesson 19

I. Check Test. Write each spelling word.

II. Spelling Words and Phrases

parade	followed the **parade**
safety	wore **safety** glasses
basement	went into the **basement**
grapefruit	an apple and a **grapefruit**
savings	**savings** in the bank
changing	**changing** the flat tire
ashamed	**ashamed** to tell
apron	a red-checked **apron**
April	**April** showers
navy	**navy** blue sweater
famous	**famous** last words
favor	did us a **favor**
ladies	**ladies** and gentlemen
nature	the world of **nature**
nation	traveled across the **nation**
station	turned to another **station**
plantation	southern **plantation**
information	dialed for **information**
betray	to **betray** a friend
worse	**worse** than before

III. Find a Fit. Write each word in its correct shape.

a.
b.
c.
d.
e.
f.
g.
h.
i.
j.
k.
l.
m.
n.
o.
p.
q.
r.
s.
t.

Other Word Forms

paraded, parading, parades, safe, safest, safely, basements, grapefruits, save, saving, change, changed, changes, shame, ashamedly, aprons, Apr., navies, fame, favored, favorite, lady, natures, natural, national, stations, stationed, plantations, inform, informed, informing, informer, betrayed, betrayal, worst

IV. Add and Subtract. Complete each puzzle to find a spelling word. Write the word.

a. plant + station – st = a large farm   _____

b. lad + tries – tr = women   _____

c. favorite – ite = an act of kindness   _____

d. as + ham + bed – b = feeling guilt   _____

e. c + hang + ring – r = making different   _____

f. in + form + station – st = facts and figures   _____

g. be + stray – s = double-cross   _____

h. sad + feet + by – bed = freedom from danger   _____

i. gray – y + pen – n + fruit = a citrus fruit   _____

j. slave + kings – elk = money in the bank   _____

k. no + station – ost = a country   _____

l. tape + rile – tee = a month   _____

m. way + horse – hay = less good   _____

n. fame + to + us – et = well-known   _____

o. part + ade – t = a grand march   _____

p. state + lion – el = a train stop   _____

q. signature – sig = outdoor world   _____

r. cap + round – cud = a cook's protective garment   _____

s. nap + wavy – paw = a branch of the armed forces   _____

t. base + statement – state = cellar   _____

Spelling Words

*parade safety basement grapefruit savings changing
ashamed apron April navy famous favor ladies nature
nation station plantation information betray worse*

V. Guide Words. These word pairs are guide words from the **Glossary/SPELLEX®**. Write the words from the spelling list that appear on the same page as each **pair** of guide words.

Example:

fifteen—freedom
_____*flew*_____
_____*forward*_____

appoint—bait
1. _____
2. _____
3. _____

balloon—bottom
4. _____
5. _____

captain—chosen
6. _____

everywhere—festive
7. _____
8. _____

freeze—graze
9. _____

help—ironing
10. _____

known—machine
11. _____

mud—offer
12. _____
13. _____
14. _____

often—pasture
15. _____

patch—preparing
16. _____

reply—scarf
17. _____
18. _____

skirt—strain
19. _____

western—wrist
20. _____

VI. **Break the Code.** Use the code to write the spelling words.

a	b	c	d	e	f	g	h	i	j	k	l	m
↕	↕	↕	↕	↕	↕	↕	↕	↕	↕	↕	↕	↕
z	y	x	w	v	u	t	s	r	q	p	o	n

a. zkilm _____

b. hgzgrlm _____

c. yvgizb _____

d. zhsznvw _____

e. tizkvuifrg _____

f. uznlfh _____

g. dlihv _____

h. mzgrlm _____

i. ozwrvh _____

j. hzuvgb _____

k. yzhvnvmg _____

l. mzeb _____

m. rmulinzgrlm _____

n. hzermth _____

o. xszmtrmt _____

p. zkiro _____

q. kzizwv _____

r. uzeli _____

s. mzgfiv _____

t. kozmgzgrlm _____

VII. **All in a Sentence.** Write all of the spelling words in sentences. Use as many **Other Word Forms** (p. 75) as you can. Circle the spelling words and the other word forms you used.

Example: *I listen to my* (favorite) *radio* (stations) .

VIII. **Final Test.** Write each spelling word.

Lesson 20

I. Check Test. Write each spelling word.

II. Spelling Words and Phrases

gulf	sailed across the **gulf**
judge	to **judge** the contest
crush	will **crush** the ice
thumb	a broken **thumb**
stump	the **stump** of the tree
studies	**studies** for the test
struck	**struck** by lightning
uncle	my aunt and **uncle**
bundle	a **bundle** of dirty laundry
jungle	tigers in the **jungle**
puzzle	a piece of the **puzzle**
upper	into the **upper** bunk
sunny	across the **sunny** meadow
muddy	with **muddy** shoes
stubborn	a **stubborn** mule
button	lost the top **button**
cutting	**cutting** the lawn
putting	**putting** on boots
current	swam against the **current**
swallow	will **swallow** the juice

III. Find a Fit. Write each word in its correct shape.

a.
b.
c.
d.
e.
f.
g.
h.
i.
j.
k.
l.
m.
n.
o.
p.
q.
r.
s.
t.

Other Word Forms

gulfs, judges, judged, judging, crushes, crushed, crushing, thumbs, stumps, stumped, study, studied, studying, strike, uncles, bundles, bundled, bundling, jungles, puzzled, puzzling, up, sun, sunnier, sunniest, mud, muddier, muddiest, stubbornly, stubbornest, buttons, buttoned, cut, cuts, cutter, put, puts, currents, currently, swallowed

IV. Find the Right Box. In alphabetical order, write the spelling words in the correct boxes.

Double Letters	Consonant + *le*	One-syllable Words
1. _____	1. _____	1. _____
2. _____	2. _____	2. _____
3. _____	3. _____	3. _____
4. _____	4. _____	4. _____
5. _____		5. _____
6. _____		6. _____
7. _____		
8. _____		
9. _____		
10. _____		

What word is found in two boxes? _____

What word is not found in any box? _____

V. Hink Pink. The solution to each Hink Pink requires two rhyming words, each with one syllable. Solve each Hink Pink. One word of each Hink Pink will be a spelling word.

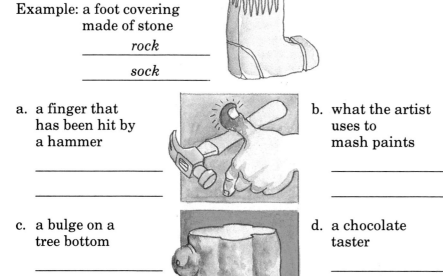

Example: a foot covering
made of stone

_____ *rock* _____

_____ *sock* _____

a. a finger that
has been hit by
a hammer

_____

_____

b. what the artist
uses to
mash paints

_____

_____

c. a bulge on a
tree bottom

_____

_____

d. a chocolate
taster

_____

_____

Spelling Words

gulf   judge   crush   thumb   stump   studies   struck
uncle   bundle   jungle   puzzle   upper   sunny   muddy
stubborn   button   cutting   putting   current   swallow

VI. Hinky Pinky. The solution to each Hinky Pinky requires two rhyming words, each with two syllables. One word of each Hinky Pinky will be a spelling word.

Example: a band member who plays only in June, July, and August

summer

drummer

a. a happy rabbit

b. the navel of a lamb

c. the evening meal eaten in the attic

d. an empty bird

e. a friend who fell on wet ground

VII. Circles and Squares. Join circle syllables with square syllables to form words from the spelling list. Write the words.

Circles: (stud) (puz) (swal) (cut) (up) (un) (bun) (cur) (sun) (jun) (put) (stub) (but) (mud)

Squares: [born] [ting] [dle] [per] [zle] [low] [rent] [dy] [ton] [cle] [gle] [ny] [ies]

a. _____   d. _____   h. _____   l. _____

b. _____   e. _____   i. _____   m. _____

c. _____   f. _____   j. _____   n. _____

g. _____   k. _____

81

VIII. Problems. Solve the problems by using these six spelling words:

judge	struck	gulf	thumb	stump	crush

    a. Write the word that ends in a silent consonant.   _____

    b. Write the word that ends in a silent vowel.   _____

    c. Write the two words that can change *u* to *a* to make two new words.   _____

        _____

    d. Write the word that names a body of water.   _____

    e. Write the word that names what the car did to the tree.   _____

IX. All in a Sentence. Use each of the spelling words in sentences about one of the following titles. Use as many **Other Word Forms** (p. 79) as you can. Circle the spelling words and the other word forms you used.

<u>A Tropical Island</u> or <u>The Cheat</u>

Example: *The tropical* (*sun*) *is very hot.*

X. Final Test. Write each spelling word.

82

Lesson 21

I. Check Test. Write each spelling word.

II. Spelling Words and Phrases

attack	after the **attack**
attached	**attached** to the house
cabbage	a small head of **cabbage**
planning	**planning** a party
passenger	an extra **passenger**
ragged	cut by the **ragged** edge
gallon	**gallon** of cold cider
valley	echoed across the **valley**
arrow	lost another **arrow**
carries	**carries** a heavier load
carried	was **carried** home
married	were **married** today
sparrow	a nesting **sparrow**
barrel	a **barrel** of pickles
allow	will **allow** us to go
bitter	a **bitter** taste
mirror	a crack in the **mirror**
potato	one baked **potato**
tomato	lettuce and **tomato**
envied	**envied** their courage

III. Find a Fit. Write each word in its correct shape.

a.
b.
c.
d.
e.
f.
g.
h.
i.
j.
k.
l.
m.
n.
o.
p.
q.
r.
s.
t.

Other Word Forms

attacks, attacked, attacker, attach, attaches, cabbages, plan, plans, planned, planner, passengers, rag, rags, gallons, valleys, arrows, carry, carrying, carrier, marry, marries, marrying, sparrows, barrels, allows, allowed, allowing, allowance, bitterly, mirrors, potatoes, tomatoes, envy, envious

Categories. Below are several categories with one word under each. Choose a spelling word for each category.

a. Things Growing Underground

beet, _____

b. People Who Ride

engineer, _____

c. Vegetables in Heads

lettuce, _____

d. Birds

robin, _____

e. Red Things to Eat

apple, _____

f. Tastes

sour, _____

g. Measures

pint, _____

h. Containers

bottle, _____

i. Pointed Things

dart, _____

j. Types of Land

hill, _____

k. Breakable Things

dish, _____

V. **Sequences and Consequences.** Show what might happen next by using these nine spelling words.

allow   attached   attack   carried   carries
envied   married   planning   ragged

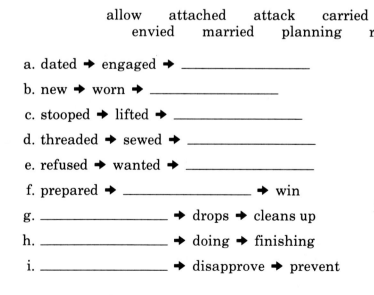

a. dated ➔ engaged ➔ _____

b. new ➔ worn ➔ _____

c. stooped ➔ lifted ➔ _____

d. threaded ➔ sewed ➔ _____

e. refused ➔ wanted ➔ _____

f. prepared ➔ _____ ➔ win

g. _____ ➔ drops ➔ cleans up

h. _____ ➔ doing ➔ finishing

i. _____ ➔ disapprove ➔ prevent

Spelling Words

attack attached cabbage planning passenger ragged
gallon valley arrow carries carried married sparrow
barrel allow bitter mirror potato tomato envied

VI. Word Search. The spelling words and some **Other Word Forms** (p. 83) can be found in the word puzzle. The words appear across and down. Circle and write the words.

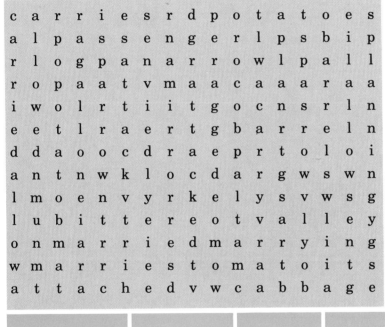

c	a	r	r	i	e	s	r	d	p	o	t	a	t	o	e	s
a	l	p	a	s	s	e	n	g	e	r	l	p	s	b	i	p
r	l	o	g	p	a	n	a	r	r	o	w	l	p	a	l	l
r	o	p	a	a	t	v	m	a	a	c	a	a	a	r	a	a
i	w	o	l	r	t	i	i	t	g	o	c	n	s	r	l	n
e	e	t	l	r	a	e	r	t	g	b	a	r	r	e	l	n
d	d	a	o	o	c	d	r	a	e	p	r	t	o	l	o	i
a	n	t	n	w	k	l	o	c	d	a	r	g	w	s	w	n
l	m	o	e	n	v	y	r	k	e	l	y	s	v	w	s	g
l	u	b	i	t	t	e	r	e	o	t	v	a	l	l	e	y
o	n	m	a	r	r	i	e	d	m	a	r	r	y	i	n	g
w	m	a	r	r	i	e	s	t	o	m	a	t	o	i	t	s
a	t	t	a	c	h	e	d	v	w	c	a	b	b	a	g	e

Other Word Forms

Across
1.
2.
3.
4.

Down
1.
2.
3.
4.
5.
6.

Spelling Words

Across
1.
2.
3.
4.
5.
6.
7.
8.
9.
10.

Down
1.
2.
3.
4.
5.
6.
7.
8.
9.
10.

85

VII. Writing Sentences. Write each set of words in a sentence. You may use **Other Word Forms** (p. 83).

1. gallon—barrel—bitter

2. married—planning—allow

3. envied—passenger—carried

4. ragged—arrow—carries

5. valley—sparrow—cabbage

6. potato—tomato—attack

7. mirror—attached

VIII. Final Test. Write each spelling word.

Lesson 22

I. **Check Test.** Write each spelling word.

II. **Spelling Words and Phrases**

cliff	the edge of the **cliff**
thrill	the **thrill** of winning
unwilling	**unwilling** to give up
silly	a **silly** reason
ribbon	tied a yellow **ribbon**
village	the **village** post office
million	into a **million** pieces
different	**different** from the others
finger	a paper cut on my **finger**
listen	will stop, look, and **listen**
chimney	cleaned the **chimney**
pilgrims	traveled with the **pilgrims**
signal	watching for the **signal**
finish	a close **finish**
midnight	stayed up until **midnight**
bridge	felt the **bridge** shaking
minute	had one more **minute**
cities	several eastern **cities**
building	the **building** site
compass	lost without a **compass**

III. **Find a Fit.** Write each word in its correct shape.

a.
b.
c.
d.
e.
f.
g.
h.
i.
j.
k.
l.
m.
n.
o.
p.
q.
r.
s.
t.

Other Word Forms
cliffs, thrills, thrilled, thriller, will, unwillingly, sillier, silliest, ribbons, villages, villager, millionaire, differ, differently, fingered, fingering, listened, listener, chimneys, pilgrim, pilgrimage, signals, signaled, signaling, finishes, finished, finishing, midnights, night, bridges, bridged, bridging, minutes, city, buildings, builds, built, builder, compasses

IV. Compare and Contrast. Use each of the spelling words in one of the phrases below.

a. not a _____ , but a smokestack

b. not a tunnel, but a _____

c. not an hour, but a _____

d. not a map, but a _____

e. not the same, but _____

f. not villages, but _____

g. not a _____ , but a thousand

h. not a canyon, but a _____

i. not destroying, but _____

j. not a warning, but a _____

k. not a city, but a _____

l. not _____ , but noon

m. not willing, but _____

n. not _____ , but serious

o. not a bore, but a _____

p. not settlers, but _____

q. not _____ , but speak

r. not a _____ , but a toe

s. not string, but _____

t. not start, but _____

V. Mix and Match. Match the first syllables in Column 1 with the last syllables in Column 2. Write the words.

Column 1	Column 2	
a. com	ish	a. _____ *compass* _____
b. sil	ute	b. _____
c. lis	ger	c. _____
d. chim	lion	d. _____
e. sig	ten	e. _____
f. fin	grims	f. _____
g. mid	bon	g. _____
h. min	pass	h. _____
i. pil	nal	i. _____
j. fin	ing	j. _____
k. mil	ies	k. _____
l. build	ly	l. _____
m. rib	lage	m. _____
n. cit	night	n. _____
o. vil	ney	o. _____

88

Spelling Words

cliff thrill unwilling silly ribbon village million different finger listen chimney pilgrims signal finish midnight bridge minute cities building compass

VI. Bases, Prefixes, and Suffixes. The spelling list contains fourteen base words and six words with prefixes, suffixes, or both. Write each spelling word.

Words With Prefixes, Suffixes, or Both	Base Words
a. millionaire	_____
b. listener	_____
c. finishes	_____
d. villager	_____
e. signaled	_____
f. ribbons	_____
g. bridging	_____
h. fingered	_____
i. minutes	_____
j. silliest	_____
k. thriller	_____
l. compasses	_____
m. cliffs	_____
n. chimneys	_____
o. _____	differ
p. _____	city
q. _____	night
r. _____	pilgrim
s. _____	will
t. _____	build

VII. All in a Row.
Write the twenty spelling words in alphabetical order. Then join the boxed letters and write four hidden words.

1. ☐ __ __ __ __ ☐
2. __ __ __ ☐ __ __ __ __
3. __ __ ☐ __ __ __ __
4. __ __ __ __ ☐
5. __ __ __ __ ☐

Hidden Word: _____

11. __ __ __ __ ☐ __ __ __
12. __ __ __ __ __ __ ☐
13. __ __ __ __ ☐ ☐
14. __ __ __ __ ☐ __ __
15. __ __ __ __ __ ☐

Hidden Word: _____

6. __ __ __ ☐ ☐ __ __
7. __ __ __ __ __ ☐ __ __ __
8. __ __ __ __ ☐ __
9. __ __ ☐ __ __ __
10. __ __ __ ☐ __ __

Hidden Word: _____

16. __ __ __ ☐ ☐ __
17. __ ☐ __ __ __
18. __ __ __ __ ☐ __
19. __ __ __ ☐ __ __ __ ☐ __
20. __ __ __ __ __ ☐ __

Hidden Word: _____

VIII. All in a Sentence.
Using **Other Word Forms** (p. 87), write a news article for your local paper about a robbery that might have occurred last night. Circle the other word forms.

Example: *Police now have him sweeping* (chimneys) *and cleaning* (buildings) *until he learns to see things* (differently).

IX. Final Test.
Write each spelling word.

I. Check Test. Write each spelling word.

II. Spelling Words and Phrases

colt	frisky **colt**
owe	whatever we **owe**
knowing	**knowing** the answer
known	if only they had **known**
growth	spoke of their **growth**
throat	a sore **throat**
cocoa	a cup of hot **cocoa**
someone	asked **someone** else
somehow	will do it **somehow**
somewhat	was **somewhat** different
somewhere	**somewhere** in the cellar
comfort	**comfort** of the campfire
company	**company** for dinner
colored	**colored** tablecloth
monthly	arrived **monthly**
wonder	made us **wonder**
choice	had no **choice**
voices	**voices** in the darkness
appointment	forgot the **appointment**
organ	played the **organ**

III. Find a Fit. Write each word in its correct shape.

a.

b.

c.

d.

e.

f.

g.

h.

i.

j.

k.

l.

m.

n.

o.

p.

q.

r.

s.

t.

Other Word Forms

colts, owes, owed, owing, know, knew, knows, knowledge, grows, grew, growing, grower, throats, comforted, comforting, comfortable, companies, companion, color, colorful, month, wondered, wondering, wonderful, wonderfully, choices, choicest, voice, voiced, voicing, appoints, appointed, organs

IV. Compare the *O* Sounds.
There is an *o* sound in each of the spelling words. In alphabetical order, write the spelling words in the correct boxes.

Long *o* as in *cold*

1. _____
2. _____
3. _____
4. _____
5. _____
6. _____
7. _____

First Syllable Having *o* With the Sound of *u* as in *cup*

1. _____
2. _____
3. _____
4. _____
5. _____
6. _____
7. _____
8. _____
9. _____

Words With *oi* Combination

1. _____
2. _____
3. _____

First Syllable Having *o* Controlled by *r*

1. _____

V. Word Match-ups.
Find a word in the spelling list that best fits each phrase or word below. Check your answers in the **Glossary/SPELLEX®**.

a. young male horse _____
b. an unknown place _____
c. inside your neck _____
d. musical instrument _____
e. hot drink _____
f. an increase _____
g. something chosen _____
h. scheduled meeting _____
i. periodically _____
j. needed for a chorus _____

k. some person _____
l. learned _____
m. debtor's problem _____
n. relieve from fear _____
o. slightly _____
p. miracle _____
q. understanding _____
r. not black-and-white _____
s. house guests _____
t. one way or another _____

Spelling Words

colt owe knowing known growth throat cocoa someone somehow somewhat somewhere comfort company colored monthly wonder choice voices appointment organ

VI. Find the Missing Treasure.

1. ltoc
2. rgoan
3. wogrth
4. tathro
5. acooc
6. doclore
7. odwner
8. rtofmoc
9. ochice
10. wongkni
11. sevoic
12. mylonth

a. Solve the scrambles and write the words.

1. __ __ ☐ __
2. __ __ ☐ __ __
3. __ __ ☐ __ __ __
4. __ __ __ ☐ __ __
5. __ __ __ __ ☐
6. __ __ __ __ __ __ ☐

7. __ __ __ ☐ __ __
8. ☐ __ __ __ __ __ __
9. __ __ ☐ __ __ __
10. __ ☐ __ __ __ __
11. __ __ __ __ __ ☐ __
12. __ __ ☐ __ __ __ __

b. Now unscramble the boxed letters into three words. What is in the treasure chest? _____ _____ _____

c. Use the words below to complete the sentence. Then you will know what to do with your treasure.

known   company   owe   appointment

You (1.) _____ it to yourself to set up an (2.) _____ with the bank and let it be (3.) _____ that you wish to purchase a computer (4.) _____ . Hooray!

93

VII. Fan Out. Write the compound words.

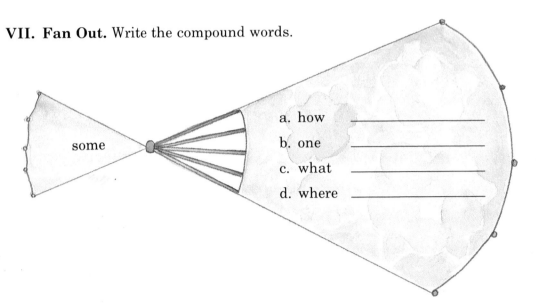

some

a. how _____

b. one _____

c. what _____

d. where _____

VIII. Many Meanings. Each pair of questions shows two uses of a spelling word. Use the **Glossary/SPELLEX**® to help you decide the meaning of the spelling word in each question. Write the spelling word in a sentence that answers each question.

a. 1. What kinds of food do you serve to <u>company</u>?

   2. What <u>company</u> printed this book?

b. 1. What gives you <u>comfort</u> when you're afraid?

   2. How can you <u>comfort</u> a little child?

c. 1. What is you first <u>choice</u> for dinner tonight?

   2. Do you have a <u>choice</u> about what you will do in the next hour?

d. 1. What fills you with <u>wonder</u>?

   2. Do you <u>wonder</u> at tall buildings?

IX. Final Test. Write each spelling word.

1	2	3	4	5
April	navy	nation	information	worse
muddy	judge	current	stubborn	struck
attack	carried	allow	planning	attached
village	bridge	signal	cities	minute
knowing	company	cocoa	someone	somewhere

I. Quotable Quotes. Use other word forms to replace the spelling words printed under each blank. Four words have no other word forms. If you need help, use the **Glossary/SPELLEX®**.

a. The _____ _____ refused to change their minds,"
       judge   stubborn
the senator added.

b. "The _____ _____ will _____ more
        cities   bridge   carried
traffic than we had planned," _____ replied.
                               someone

c. The president said, "Several _____ have _____
                                  nation   allow
both _____ to purchase _____ beans."
      company   cocoa

d. "The _____ base is located _____ in California,"
         navy   somewhere
Jay answered.

e. The general stated, "In _____ , the planes _____
                            minute   attack
the _____ beyond Pearl Harbor."
     village

f. "In _____ , we had _____ to _____
        April   planning   attached
new switches to all the traffic _____ ," the safety officer remarked.
                                  signal

g. The coach added, "I was _____ that the _____
                            information   muddy
fields present the _____ problems to the players."
                    worse

h. "We now _____ that strong wind _____ will cause
            knowing   current
the storm to _____ in the early morning hours," the newscaster
              struck
reported.

1	2	3	4	5
changing	favor	station	swallow	betray
sunny	puzzle	button	bundle	choice
married	mirror	savings	carries	thrill
listen	finish	wonder	comfort	appointment
throat	ribbon	cliff	potato	tomato

II. Word Building. Add word parts to each spelling word or its base word to make other word forms. If you need help, use the **Glossary/SPELLEX®**.

Spelling Words	*s or es*	*ed*	*ing*
Example: walking	*walks*	*walked*	
a. changing	_____	_____	
b. married	_____		_____
c. listen	_____	_____	_____
d. throat	_____		
e. favor	_____	_____	_____
f. puzzle	_____	_____	_____
g. mirror	_____	_____	_____
h. finish	_____	_____	_____
i. station	_____	_____	_____
j. button	_____	_____	_____
k. savings	_____	_____	_____
l. tomato	_____		
m. cliff	_____		
n. swallow	_____	_____	_____
o. bundle	_____	_____	_____
p. carries		_____	_____
q. comfort	_____	_____	_____
r. potato	_____		
s. betray	_____	_____	_____
t. thrill	_____	_____	_____
u. choice	_____		
v. wonder	_____	_____	_____
w. appointment	_____	_____	_____
x. ribbon	_____		
y. sunny	_____	_____	_____

1	2	3	4	5
safety	grapefruit	cutting	thumb	crush
ragged	barrel	silly	building	voices
chimney	owe	growth	monthly	colt
gallon	pilgrims	cabbage	sparrow	arrow
parade	ladies	plantation	putting	studies

III. Classified Ads. Complete each ad by writing other word forms or the spelling words. Use each word or its other word form only once. If you need help, use the **Glossary/SPELLEX®**.

a. Gardener ad: We hire green (4) __ __ __ __ __ __ only.

b. Roof cleaner ad: All (1) __ __ __ __ __ __ __ __ swept clean.

c. The *Mayflower* captain ad:
Only (2) __ __ __ __ __ __ __ __ need apply.

d. Robin Hood ad: We rent bows and (5) __ __ __ __ __ __ .

e. Comedian ad: A lot of (3) __ __ __ __ __ __ __ __ __ accepted.

f. Coleslaw maker ad: Firm (3) __ __ __ __ __ __ __ __ required.

g. Fancy (2) __ __ __ __ __ __ __ __ __ __ grower ad:
We sell juice by the (1) __ __ __ __ __ __ __ .

h. Bird seller ad: Buy (4) __ __ __ __ __ __ __ __ cheap.

i. Choir director ad: Add your (5) __ __ __ __ __ to ours.

j. Traffic guard ad: We promise you a (1) __ __ __ __ crossing.

k. Self-defense instructor ad:
We deal (5) __ __ __ __ __ __ __ __ blows.

l. Diet planner ad: Eat right and (3) __ __ __ __ slender.

m. Southern realtor ad:
Old (3) __ __ __ __ __ __ __ __ __ __ __ bought and sold.

n. Writer ad: Go from (1) __ __ __ __ to riches.

o. Carpenter ad: We (4) __ __ __ __ __ your dreams.

p. Calendar maker ad: The weeks grow into (4) __ __ __ __ __ __ .

q. Stable owner ad: We rent spring (5) __ __ __ __ __ .

r. Tutor ad: You can (5) __ __ __ __ __ with a buddy.

s. Amusement-park owner ad: Have (2) __ __ __ __ __ __ __ of fun.

t. Barber ad: We make short (3) __ __ __ __ .

u. Kennel owner ad: Let's (4) __ __ __ a dog in your life.

v. Nail filer ad: We serve (2) __ __ __ __ fingers.

w. Moneylender ad: You (2) __ __ __ it to yourself.

x. Marcher ad: No (1) __ __ __ __ __ __ __ too small.

1	2	3	4	5
famous	ashamed	nature	stump	different
upper	envied	million	known	finger
organ	basement	apron	uncle	jungle
gulf	colored	passenger	midnight	valley
bitter	compass	unwilling	somehow	somewhat

IV. Word Operations. Use words from the spelling list to complete the exercises below. If you need help, use the **Glossary/SPELLEX®**.

a. **Operation Plural.** Write the *s* or *es* form of each word. Use the **Glossary/SPELLEX®**.

1. gulf _____*gulfs*_____   7. stump _____

2. organ _____   8. uncle _____

3. million _____   9. finger _____

4. compass _____   10. jungle _____

5. apron _____   11. valley _____

6. passenger _____   12. basement _____

b. **Operation Adverb.** Write an other word form that ends in *ly* for each word. Use the **Glossary/SPELLEX®** to check your work. The starred words are difficult.

1. bitter _____   *6. nature _____

2. different _____   *7. known _____

3. famous _____   8. unwilling _____

*4. envied _____   9. ashamed _____

*5. colored _____

c. **Operation Addition.** Add the word parts to make spelling words. Write the words. You will have to add a letter to one word to make the spelling word.

1. some + what = _____   3. up + er = _____

2. mid + night = _____   4. some + how = _____

Lesson 25

I. Check Test. Write each spelling word.

II. Spelling Words and Phrases

ugly	**ugly** storm
public	open to the **public**
husband	**husband** and wife
pumpkin	turned into a **pumpkin**
multiply	learned to **multiply**
thunder	afraid of **thunder**
salty	too **salty** to eat
altered	**altered** their plans
false	true or **false**
smaller	**smaller** or larger
stalk	a **stalk** of corn
awful	thought it was **awful**
crawl	had to **crawl** out
drawn	**drawn** by the artist
drawing	tore the **drawing** paper
watered	**watered** the garden
cough	a dose of **cough** medicine
bought	**bought** my own lunch
brought	**brought** our friend
calm	**calm** and peaceful

III. Find a Fit. Write each word in its correct shape.

a.
b.
c.
d.
e.
f.
g.
h.
i.
j.
k.
l.
m.
n.
o.
p.
q.
r.
s.
t.

Other Word Forms

uglier, ugliest, publicity, publicly, publicize, husbands, pumpkins, multiplies, multiplying, multiplier, thundering, salt, salting, alter, alters, falsely, small, smallest, stalked, stalking, awfully, crawls, crawled, draw, drew, water, watering, watery, coughed, coughs, coughing, buy, buying, bring, bringing, calmer, calmest, calmly

99

IV. Scrambled Words. Unscramble the words in each of the columns. Then rearrange the boxed letters to form a word from the spelling list. If your answers are correct, you will have uncovered all the spelling words.

a. wnadr   __ __ ☐ __ __

b. undreth   ☐ __ __ __ __ __

c. slafe   __ __ ☐ __ __

d. rasmell   __ __ ☐ __ __ __

e. tilumply __ __ __ __ __ __ __ ☐

Word from the spelling list: __ __ __ __ __

f. driwang   __ __ __ __ __ __ ☐

g. ghuco   __ ☐ __ __ __

h. redlate   __ __ ☐ __ __ __

i. wlacr   __ ☐ __ __ __

j. ghtobu   __ __ __ ☐ __ __

k. gluy   ☐ __ __ __

l. blicup   __ __ ☐ __ __ __

Word from the spelling list:

__ __ __ __ __ __

m. handbus   __ __ ☐ __ __ __ __

n. fuwal   ☐ __ __ __ __

o. nimpkup   __ __ __ __ ☐ __ __

p. redweat   __ __ ☐ __ __ __ __

q. aclm   __ __ ☐ __

Word from the spelling list: __ __ __ __ __

100

Spelling Words

ugly public husband pumpkin multiply thunder salty altered false smaller stalk awful crawl drawn drawing watered cough bought brought calm

V. Generally Speaking. Write each spelling word in the group it best fits.

a. small, _____ , smallest

b. poor, bad, _____

c. sketching, painting, _____

d. male, spouse, _____

e. wrong, untrue, _____

f. changed, fitted, _____

g. sniff, sneeze, _____

h. wet, sprayed, _____

i. spicy, seasoned, _____

j. unattractive, unpleasant, _____

k. squash, cucumber, _____

l. sketched, painted, _____

m. windless, motionless, _____

n. storm, lightning, _____

o. add, subtract, _____

p. creep, _____ , walk

q. purchased, shopped, _____

r. took, carried, _____

s. stem, trunk, _____

t. citizens, people, _____

VI. Base Words.
The spelling list contains twelve base words and eight words that are not base words. Write each spelling word.

Words That Are Not Base Words	Base Words		Words That Are Not Base Words	Base Words
a. multiplying	*multiply*	k. awfully		
b. publicly		l. ugliest		
c. falsely		m.		small
d. calmly		n.		draw
e. coughing		o.		buy
f. husbands		p.		bring
g. thundering		q.		salt
h. stalked		r.		water
i. pumpkins		s.		draw
j. crawled		t.		alter

VII. Poetry Corner.
Using **Other Word Forms** (p. 99), make up titles for poems. Circle the other word forms.

Example: *The Baby* (*Crawls*)

VIII. Final Test.
Write each spelling word.

Lesson 26

I. Check Test. Write each spelling word.

II. Spelling Words and Phrases

eighteen	**eighteen** students
eighty	**eighty** days
weigh	to **weigh** and measure
neighborhood	a friendly **neighborhood**
plain	**plain** wrapper
raise	had to **raise** it higher
maintain	to **maintain** order
ashes	burned to **ashes**
badge	showed your **badge**
flashlight	the dimming **flashlight**
edge	at the **edge** of the wharf
else	nothing **else** to do
kettle	heated the **kettle**
settle	to **settle** in the town
freckles	covered with **freckles**
quest	their **quest** for gold
question	asked another **question**
mention	the **mention** of my name
western	wore **western** clothes
cherries	a basket of **cherries**

III. Find a Fit. Write each word in its correct shape.

a.
b.
c.
d.
e.
f.
g.
h.
i.
j.
k.
l.
m.
n.
o.
p.
q.
r.
s.
t.

Other Word Forms
eighteenth, eightieth, weight, weighed, neighbor, neighboring, neighborly, plainly, plainer, plainest, raises, raised, raising, maintained, maintenance, ash, badges, flashlights, edges, edging, edgy, kettles, settler, settled, freckled, questing, questions, mentioned, mentioning, west, westerly, cherry

IV. Word Search. Find each of the spelling words in the grid below. The words appear across and down. Circle and write the words.

```
q u e s t i o n a t n e
v j s w e s t e r n a r
l o r a i s e i r l j m
f l a s h l i g h t k e
r e v m e i g h t e e n
e t l e d b o b y v m t
c w e i g h a o p s a i
k p l g e v s r l e i o
l r s h w m h h a t n n
e k e t t l e o i t t d
s j s y v m s o n l a t
q u e s t b a d g e i d
c h e r r i e s t i n d
```

Across

1. ⬚⬚⬚⬚⬚⬚⬚
2. ⬚⬚⬚⬚⬚⬚⬚
3. ⬚⬚⬚⬚⬚⬚
4. ⬚⬚⬚⬚⬚⬚⬚⬚

5. ⬚⬚⬚⬚⬚⬚⬚
6. ⬚⬚⬚⬚⬚
7. ⬚⬚⬚⬚⬚
8. ⬚⬚⬚⬚⬚
9. ⬚⬚⬚⬚⬚
10. ⬚⬚⬚⬚⬚⬚⬚⬚

Down

1. ⬚⬚⬚⬚⬚⬚⬚
2. ⬚⬚⬚
3. ⬚⬚⬚⬚⬚
4. ⬚⬚⬚⬚
5. ⬚⬚⬚⬚
6. ⬚⬚⬚⬚⬚⬚⬚⬚⬚⬚
7. ⬚⬚⬚⬚
8. ⬚⬚⬚⬚⬚⬚
9. ⬚⬚⬚⬚⬚⬚⬚
10. ⬚⬚⬚⬚⬚⬚⬚

V. Build a Word. Write the four spelling words that use *eigh* to make the long *a* sound.

a. _____ b. _____ c. _____ d. _____

Spelling Words

eighteen   eighty   weigh   neighborhood   plain   raise
maintain   ashes   badge   flashlight   edge   else   kettle
settle   freckles   quest   question   mention   western   cherries

VI. Antonyms. Find an antonym from the spelling list to complete each puzzle.
Write each word.

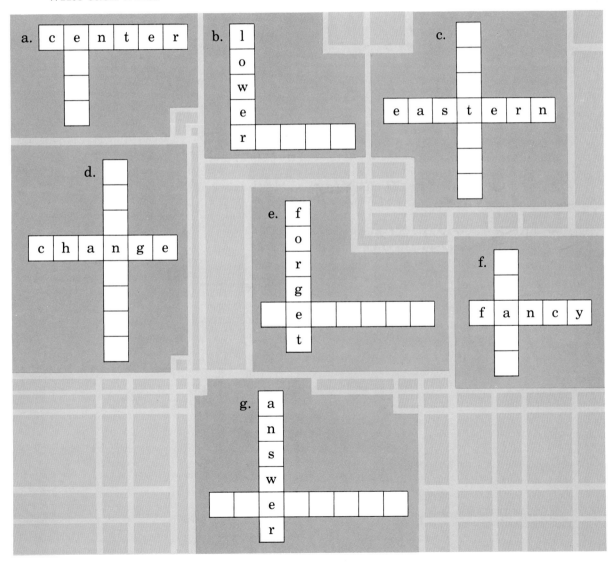

a. c e n t e r

b. l o w e r

c. e a s t e r n

d. c h a n g e

e. f o r g e t

f. f a n c y

g. a n s w e r

VII. Generally Speaking. Write a spelling word in the group it best fits.

a. logs, fireplace, _____

b. lantern, lamp, _____

c. grapes, blueberries, _____

d. pot, pan, _____

e. medal, pin, _____

f. ordinary, simple, _____

g. keep, continue, _____

VIII. Missing Vowel. The following words from the list are missing the same vowel. Write the words.

a. ___ ls ___

b. s ___ ttl ___

c. qu ___ st

d. fr ___ ckl ___ s

e. ___ dg ___

f. m ___ ntion

g. w ___ st ___ rn

h. qu ___ stion

i. rais ___

a. _____

b. _____

c. _____

d. _____

e. _____

f. _____

g. _____

h. _____

i. _____

IX. Write Your Journal. Use each of the spelling words or **Other Word Forms** (p. 103) to write a page in your journal about the day you and your family moved. Circle the spelling words and the other word forms you used.

Date:

X. Final Test. Write each spelling word.

Lesson 27

I. Check Test. Write each spelling word.

II. Spelling Words and Phrases

deaf	thought I was **deaf**
heavy	looks very **heavy**
health	in good **health**
treasure	buried **treasure**
meadow	ran through the **meadow**
feather	a bird's **feather**
leather	dressed in **leather**
sweater	has put on a **sweater**
headquarters	visit to the **headquarters**
except	**except** on Sunday
erect	will **erect** a building
select	will **select** another color
direct	had to **direct** traffic
protect	to **protect** them from disease
export	the **export** of wheat
regular	on a **regular** basis
festival	the annual **festival**
remember	if you don't **remember**
necktie	struggled with my **necktie**
president	may meet a **president**

III. Find a Fit. Write each word in its correct shape.

a.
b.
c.
d.
e.
f.
g.
h.
i.
j.
k.
l.
m.
n.
o.
p.
q.
r.
s.
t.

Other Word Forms

deafen, deafness, heavier, heaviest, healthy, healthier, healthful, treasury, meadows, feathered, feathery, leathered, leathery, sweaters, excepted, exception, erected, selected, selection, directed, direction, protector, protection, exported, regularly, regulates, regulation, festive, remembrance, neckties, presidential, presidency

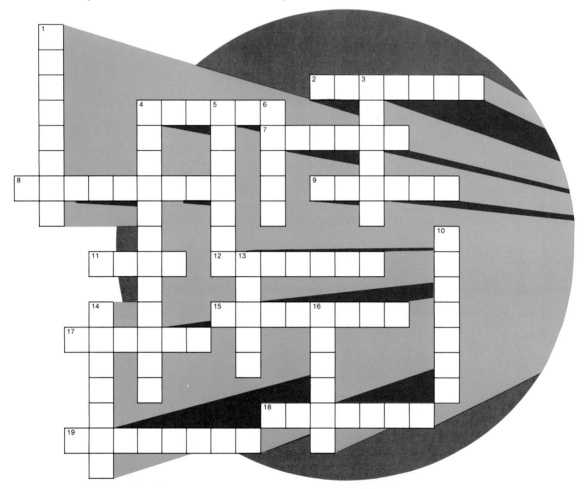

Across

2. an item of warm clothing
4. one's physical condition
7. not including
8. the leader of a nation
9. to conduct
11. unable to hear
12. usual
15. not to forget
17. to choose
18. to defend
19. a special celebration

Down

1. hidden wealth
3. to ship out of the country
4. the main office
5. tanned animal skin
6. not light in weight
10. clothing for decoration
13. up straight
14. bird clothing
16. a field

Spelling Words

deaf heavy health treasure meadow feather leather sweater headquarters except erect select direct protect export regular festival remember necktie president

V. Guide Words. These word pairs are guide words from the **Glossary/SPELLEX®**. Write the words from the spelling list that appear on the same page as each pair of guide words.

day—dropped

1. _____

2. _____

dry—escape

3. _____

everywhere—festive

4. _____

5. _____

6. _____

7. _____

great—helmet

8. _____

9. _____

10. _____

known—machine

11. _____

magazine—mountain

12. _____

mud—offer

13. _____

president—quart

14. _____

15. _____

quarter—replied

16. _____

17. _____

schoolmate—skinned

18. _____

stray—talent

19. _____

taught—ugly

20. _____

a	b	c	d	e	f	g	h	i	j	k	l	m	n	o	p	q	r	s	t	u	v	w	x	y	z
↓	↓	↓	↓	↓	↓	↓	↓	↓	↓	↓	↓	↓	↓	↓	↓	↓	↓	↓	↓	↓	↓	↓	↓	↓	↓
t	u	v	w	x	y	z	a	b	c	d	e	f	g	h	i	j	k	l	m	n	o	p	q	r	s

a. zdlhaly _____

b. zlslja _____

c. olhsao _____

d. slhaoly _____

e. yltltily _____

f. kpylja _____

g. uljrapl _____

h. aylhzbyl _____

i. mlhaoly _____

j. lejlwa _____

k. klhm _____

l. ylnbshy _____

m. lylja _____

n. olhkxbhyalyz _____

o. mlzapchs _____

p. olhcf _____

q. wyvalja _____

r. lewvya _____

s. wylzpklua _____

t. tlhkvd _____

VII. All in a Sentence. Using **Other Word Forms** (p. 107), write a TV news announcement that tells about the President's visit to your town. Circle the other word forms.

Example: *They celebrated his arrival with* (festive) *banners.*

VIII. Final Test. Write each spelling word.

Lesson 28

I. **Check Test.** Write each spelling word.

II. **Spelling Words and Phrases**

anger	filled with **anger**
angry	the **angry** mob
answer	did not **answer**
average	figured the **average**
fancy	a **fancy** decoration
calves	fed the **calves**
canal	dug the **canal**
tackle	a clean, low **tackle**
castle	defended the **castle**
fasten	will **fasten** the seat belt
platform	stood on the **platform**
magazine	our **magazine** subscription
gasoline	a red can of **gasoline**
valentine	mailed the last **valentine**
savage	the lion's **savage** roar
language	lost my **language** book
garage	waited at the **garage**
machine	an ancient flying **machine**
palm	in the **palm** of my hand
engine	started the **engine**

III. **Find a Fit.** Write each word in its correct shape.

a.
b.
c.
d.
e.
f.
g.
h.
i.
j.
k.
l.
m.
n.
o.
p.
q.
r.
s.
t.

Other Word Forms
angered, angering, angrily, angrier, angriest, answers, answered, averages, averaged, averaging, fanciful, fancier, fanciest, calf, canals, tackles, tackled, tackling, castles, fastens, fastened, fastening, fastener, platforms, magazines, valentines, savages, languages, garages, garaged, garaging, machinery, palmed, engines, engineer

IV. Hidden Words.
The spelling words can be found in the word puzzle. The words appear across and down. Circle and write the words.

Across

1.
2.
3.
4.
5.
6.
7.
8.
9.

Down

1.
2.
3.
4.
5.
6.
7.
8.
9.
10.
11.

e	n	g	i	n	e	l	f	a	s	t	e	n	p
n	m	a	c	h	i	n	e	w	v	j	m	m	a
t	a	r	v	o	m	y	f	a	n	c	y	l	l
a	g	a	s	o	l	i	n	e	l	v	r	c	m
c	a	g	a	m	a	e	g	z	c	a	n	a	l
k	z	g	v	o	n	i	e	v	w	l	w	l	o
l	i	m	a	k	g	a	r	a	g	e	a	v	c
e	n	o	g	a	u	l	a	n	a	n	n	e	a
v	e	w	e	v	a	c	r	g	n	t	s	s	s
a	v	e	r	a	g	e	v	r	g	i	w	m	t
m	a	c	h	l	e	y	c	y	e	n	e	w	l
p	l	a	t	f	o	r	m	n	r	e	r	j	e

V. Generally Speaking.
Write each spelling word in the group it best fits.

a. newspaper, journal, _____

b. fuel, oil, _____

c. palace, chateau, _____

d. speech, expression, _____

e. respond, reply, _____

f. attach, bind, _____

g. card, heart shaped, _____

h. decorated, not plain, _____

i. fuming, furious, _____

j. waterway, channel, _____

k. cows, bulls, _____

l. medium, usual, _____

m. rage, fury, _____

n. seize, undertake, _____

o. floor, stage, _____

p. motor, _____ , _____

q. drive, park, _____

r. brutal, cruel, _____

s. oak, fern, _____

Spelling Words

anger angry answer average fancy calves canal tackle castle fasten platform magazine gasoline valentine savage language garage machine palm engine

VI. Many Meanings. Complete each pair of sentences with the same spelling word. Write the meanings of the spelling word as it is used in the sentence. Use the **Glossary/SPELLEX®.**

a. 1. The weather here is too cold for growing a _____ .

   2. I have the prize in the _____ of my hand.

b. 1. I think that 6 is the _____ of 2 and 10.

   2. We have had an _____ amount of snow this year.

c. 1. I will _____ that math problem later.

   2. The team's star player made that last _____ .

d. 1. I must have left my _____ book at home.

   2. I wish I knew a _____ other than English.

VII. Writing Sentences. Use each set of words in a sentence that shows that you really can exaggerate. You may use **Other Word Forms** (p. 111).

1. machine—garage—gasoline

2. savage—anger—castle

3. average—valentine—fancy

4. engine—canal—platform

5. palm—tackle—angry

6. magazine—language—answer

7. fasten—calves

VIII. Final Test. Write each spelling word.

I. Check Test. Write each spelling word.

II. Spelling Words and Phrases

elbow	sore **elbow**
jelly	has spread the **jelly**
begged	**begged** us to come
message	received the **message**
dresser	into the **dresser** drawer
unless	**unless** you go
attend	will **attend** together
cellar	down the **cellar** stairs
tennis	learned to play **tennis**
helpful	always very **helpful**
shelter	**shelter** from the storm
lemon	orange, **lemon**, and lime
record	played the new **record**
people	elected by the **people**
recess	waiting for **recess**
secret	kept the **secret**
English	**English**, French, and Russian
period	a **period** or a comma
nearby	**nearby** field
fearful	became **fearful**

III. Find a Fit. Write each word in its correct shape.

a.
b.
c.
d.
e.
f.
g.
h.
i.
j.
k.
l.
m.
n.
o.
p.
q.
r.
s.
t.

Other Word Forms

elbows, jellies, jellied, beg, begs, begging, beggar, messages, messenger, dress, dresses, dressing, attending, attendance, cellars, helpfully, helpless, sheltered, sheltering, lemons, lemony, recorded, recording, recorder, peoples, recesses, recessed, recessing, secretly, secretive, England, periodical, periodically, fearfully, fearing

IV. Pandora's Box. Solve the puzzle by using spelling words and one **Other Word Form** (p. 115).* Use the **Glossary/SPELLEX®**. Then rearrange the four letters in the outlined squares, and you will know what was left in Pandora's box.

__ __ __ __ = _____

Across
1. the end of a sentence
6. hidden; concealed
7. a play period
8. citrus fruits*
9. a game played on a court
11. frightened
13. like jam
16. an underground room
17. pleaded
19. useful

Down
1. persons
2. furniture for clothing
3. to be present at
4. a note or letter
5. close; not faraway
10. a protective house
12. a language
14. an album
15. except if
18. a joint in the arm

Spelling Words

elbow jelly begged message dresser unless attend
cellar tennis helpful shelter lemon record people
recess secret English period nearby fearful

V. Not _____ **, But.** Use each of the spelling words in one of the phrases below.

a. not faraway, but _____

b. not useless, but _____

c. not brave, but _____

d. not a comma, but a _____

e. not _____ , but French

f. not things, but _____

g. not study period, but _____

h. not the _____ , but the attic

i. not hidden, but _____

j. not if, but _____

k. not _____ , but be absent

l. not asked, but _____

m. not a knee, but an _____

n. not a closet, but a _____

o. not peanut butter, but _____

p. not an orange, but a _____

q. not uncover, but _____

r. not golf, but _____

s. not a code, but a _____

t. not a _____ , but a tape

117

Be a Word Detective. Unscramble each word to find a word from the spelling list. Write the word.

a. sameegs   _____

b. rodepi   _____

c. corerd   _____

d. nussel   _____

e. gebged   _____

f. pleeop   _____

g. nelom   _____

h. lowbe   _____

i. lylje   _____

j. shinglE   _____

k. serces   _____

l. tteand   _____

m. sersedr   _____

n. sitenn   _____

o. fellphu   _____

p. steecr   _____

q. crella   _____

r. reffula   _____

s. branye   _____

t. treshle   _____

VII. **All in a Sentence.** Use each of the spelling words or **Other Word Forms** (p. 115) to write a note to someone you know. Tell about an event that recently happened to you. Circle the spelling words and the other word forms you used.

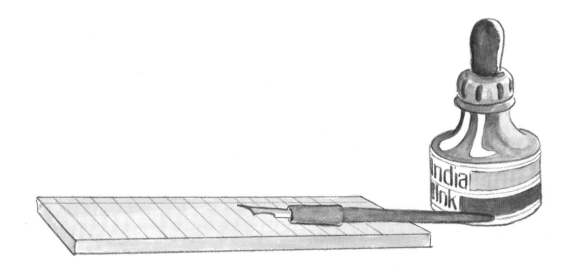

VIII. **Final Test.** Write each spelling word.

1	2	3	4	5
altered	canal	false	nearby	select
angry	deaf	fasten	palm	tennis
bought	direct	headquarters	quest	ugly
calm	eighteen	health	question	weigh
calves	English	lemon	secret	western

I. Hide and Seek. Twenty-two other word forms and three spelling words can be found in the word puzzle. The words appear down, diagonally, and across. Circle and write each word. Use the **Glossary/SPELLEX**®.

Down

1.
2.
3.
4.
5.
6.
7.

Diagonally

1.
2.
3.

```
c a l f p w e s t e r l y u q
a l n g a d i r e c t o r x u
l t m g i s b u y i n g y p e
m e t o r c t l v q u e s t s
l r v t s i l e m o n y p i t
y s k z q t e n n i s m o n i
e n g l a n d r h e u w t e o
u g l i n e s s e c r e t s n
p a l m s h r e a p n i b b e
r p o r l d x w l v a g i o d
w f a l s e l y t e b h a i c
m g r o o a u n h a c s t n a
l k j r m f u t y e o t z g n
e i g h t e e n t h p s e n a
v c r o t n d n e a r b y d l
l a m h e a d q u a r t e r s
```

Across

1.
2.
3.
4.
5.
6.
7.
8.
9.
10.
11.
12.
13.
14.
15.

119

30

1	2	3	4	5
multiply	smaller	drawing	salty	thunder
eighty	mention	freckles	cherries	settle
heavy	remember	sweater	leather	meadow
engine	average	valentine	gasoline	answer
record	helpful	attend	shelter	cellar

II. **Newspaper Headlines.** Write other word forms or the spelling words to complete the newspaper headlines. The number tells you in what column you can find the spelling word. Write each word or its other word form only once. Capitalize each word. If you need help, use the **Glossary/SPELLEX®**.

a. Town Buys New Fire (1) _____

b. Dogs (4) _____ From Cold

c. (4) _____ Blossoms Bloom

d. New Skin Cream Removes (3) _____

e. Pioneer (5) _____ on Moon

f. (4) _____ Explosion Causes Damage

g. World's (2) _____ Dog Wins Award

h. Baseball Fan (3) _____ World Series

i. (4) _____ Mine Clue to Mystery

j. Candy (3) _____ Stolen From Van

k. Farmers Plow Old (5) _____

l. Winner Breaks All (1) _____

m. Scouts' Wishes Are (5) _____

n. Thirty (5) _____ Damaged by Flood

o. Baseball (2) _____ Challenged

p. (5) _____ Herd Stampedes Village

q. Old Memories (2) _____

r. Town Celebrates (1) _____ Birthday

s. (4) _____ Hide Saves Circus Elephant

t. (1) _____ Snowfall in Years Blankets State

u. Firefighter (2) _____ Child to Safety

v. Artist (3) _____ Self-Portrait

w. Speaker (2) _____ New Plan

x. Flu Germs (1) _____ Daily

y. New Yarns Create New (3) _____

1	2	3	4	5
husband	pumpkin	drawn	brought	cough
plain	raise	ashes	flashlight	kettle
treasure	feather	erect	necktie	export
machine	magazine	savage	tackle	platform
elbow	unless	dresser	period	recess

III. Words in a Series. Use other word forms or the spelling words to complete each series. The number tells you in what column you can find the spelling word. Use each word or its other word form only once.

a. wildly, ferociously, (3) _____

b. bureaus, chests, (3) _____

c. stages, landings, (5) _____

d. shoulders, knees, (1) _____

e. pans, pots, (5) _____

f. simply, commonly, (1) _____

g. lifted, elevated, (2) _____

h. free times, breaks, (5) _____

i. squashes, gourds, (2) _____

j. built, constructed, (3) _____

k. beacons, lanterns, (4) _____

l. sneezing, choking, (5) _____

m. sent out, shipped, (5) _____

n. scarves, bow ties, (4) _____

o. pulleys, levers, (1) _____

p. commas, colons, (4) _____

q. burned material, remains, (3) _____

r. mate, partner, (1) _____

s. pamphlets, journals, (2) _____

t. if not, except if, (2) _____

u. soft, light, (2) _____

v. stopped, tripped, (4) _____

w. valuables, jewels, (1) _____

x. sketching, painting, (3) _____

y. carries, takes, (4) _____

30

1	2	3	4	5
anger	crawl	fearful	maintain	protect
awful	edge	festival	message	public
badge	else	garage	neighborhood	regular
begged	except	jelly	people	stalk
castle	fancy	language	president	watered

IV. Break the Code. Use the code to write twenty-four other word forms and one spelling word. Write each word.

a	b	c	d	e	f	g	h	i	j	k	l	m	n	o	p	q	r	s	t	u	v	w	x	y	z
↓	↓	↓	↓	↓	↓	↓	↓	↓	↓	↓	↓	↓	↓	↓	↓	↓	↓	↓	↓	↓	↓	↓	↓	↓	↓
g	d	j	r	u	e	y	w	k	a	c	p	s	h	b	n	l	m	f	o	t	w	z	v	x	i

a. qjpaejafm

b. hjufdzpa

c. sfjdseqqg

d. ldfmzbfpuzjq

e. dfaeqjdqg

f. fykfluztp

g. sjpkzfmu

h. ldtufkuztp

i. rjzpujzpm

j. rfmmfpafd

k. sfmuzxjqm

l. leoqzkqg

m. pfzanotdnttbm

n. kdjvqfd

o. mujqim

p. jpadzqg

q. kjmuqfm

r. lftlqfm

s. ojbafm

t. ofam

u. cfqqzfm

v. fbafm

w. jvseqqg

x. ajdjafm

y. fqmf

Lesson 31

I. **Check Test.** Write each spelling word.

II. **Spelling Words and Phrases**

avenue	the tree-lined **avenue**
afterward	joined them **afterward**
captain	talked with the **captain**
tablet	writing **tablet**
grandfather	went with my **grandfather**
handsome	**handsome** animal
handful	a **handful** for each of us
palace	behind the **palace** wall
factory	the new **factory**
families	several **families**
pasture	cows grazing in the **pasture**
plastic	made of **plastic**
gravel	played in the **gravel** pit
shadow	will cast a long **shadow**
piano	could play the **piano**
gathering	were **gathering** there
practicing	**practicing** each day
pajamas	red-striped **pajamas**
altogether	**altogether** satisfied
although	**although** we tried

III. **Find a Fit.** Write each word in its correct shape.

a.
b.
c.
d.
e.
f.
g.
h.
i.
j.
k.
l.
m.
n.
o.
p.
q.
r.
s.
t.

Other Word Forms
avenues, afterwards, captains, tablets, grandfathers, handsomely, handfuls, palaces, factories, family, pastures, pastured, plastics, gravels, gravelly, shadows, shadowed, shadowing, pianos, pianist, gather, gathers, gathered, practice, practices, practiced

IV. Noun or Verb. Sometimes a word may be a noun or a verb, depending on how it is used in a sentence. Find a spelling word or **Other Word Form** (p. 123) that fits in each pair of sentences. Write *N* or *V* beside each word.

a. 1. My _____ follows me everywhere.

   2. The trees will _____ him from the sun.

b. 1. You must _____ your tennis serve.

   2. Choir _____ will be held this morning.

c. 1. A crowd was _____ in the park for the concert.

   2. Sixteen grandchildren attended the family _____ .

d. 1. The cows will _____ in the upper meadow.

   2. Wild flowers grew abundantly in the _____ .

V. Twenty Words. The twenty spelling words can be found in the word puzzle. The words appear across, down, and diagonally. Circle and write the words.

Across

1.
2.
3.
4.
5.
6.
7.
8.
9.
10.
11.

a	l	t	h	o	u	g	h	s	c	l	u	a	f
m	p	m	o	h	f	a	m	i	l	i	e	s	f
r	s	a	t	p	a	s	t	u	r	e	x	w	a
h	g	c	l	i	r	n	n	a	c	r	e	p	c
c	a	p	t	a	i	n	d	v	b	n	c	r	t
m	t	n	a	n	c	i	t	f	r	l	e	a	o
s	h	a	d	o	w	e	e	r	u	t	e	c	r
e	e	n	w	s	r	e	l	f	u	l	t	t	y
j	r	a	l	t	o	g	e	t	h	e	r	i	a
g	i	p	a	j	a	m	a	s	s	a	n	c	v
a	n	e	g	r	a	v	e	l	e	t	s	i	e
i	g	r	a	n	d	f	a	t	h	e	r	n	n
a	f	t	e	r	w	a	r	d	k	a	n	g	u
p	l	a	s	t	i	c	r	e	t	o	c	e	e

Down

1.
2.
3.
4.
5.

Diagonally

1.
2.
3.
4.

Spelling Words

avenue afterward captain tablet grandfather handsome handful palace factory families pasture plastic gravel shadow piano gathering practicing pajamas altogether although

VI. Words and Meanings. Write a spelling word for each meaning. Check your answers in the **Glossary/SPELLEX®**.

a. a wide street _____

b. the leader of a group _____

c. even though _____

d. a keyboard musical instrument _____

e. coming together in a group _____

f. a building where goods are made _____

g. the home of a king or queen _____

h. several sets of parents and their children _____

i. later _____

j. the father of a person's father or mother _____

k. pebbles and small pieces of rock _____

l. totally or completely _____

m. clothing for sleeping _____

n. the amount that can be held in a person's hand _____

o. a substance that can be easily shaped _____

p. shade made by a person, animal, or object _____

q. grassland where animals graze _____

r. a pad of paper _____

s. good-looking _____

t. doing many times over to gain skill _____

VII. Words in Use. List the spelling words in any ten pairs.

a. _____ _____

b. _____ _____

c. _____ _____

d. _____ _____

e. _____ _____

f. _____ _____

g. _____ _____

h. _____ _____

i. _____ _____

j. _____ _____

Now use each pair of words in a sentence.
You may use **Other Word Forms** (p. 123).

VIII. Final Test. Write each spelling word.

Lesson 32

I. Check Test. Write each spelling word.

II. Spelling Words and Phrases

nephew	niece and **nephew**
everywhere	**everywhere** they go
entire	the **entire** day
elephant	circus **elephant**
lemonade	another **lemonade** stand
anyhow	will do it **anyhow**
anyone	if **anyone** cares
anywhere	fits **anywhere**
anyway	didn't want it **anyway**
friendly	a **friendly** wave
weather	stormy **weather**
breakfast	late for **breakfast**
liberty	**liberty** or death
visitor	greeted the **visitor**
wilderness	a **wilderness** trail
withdraw	will **withdraw** your name
industry	the steel **industry**
interest	a great deal of **interest**
install	will **install** the phone
talent	a **talent** for singing

III. Find a Fit. Write each word in its correct shape.

a.
b.
c.
d.
e.
f.
g.
h.
i.
j.
k.
l.
m.
n.
o.
p.
q.
r.
s.
t.

Other Word Forms

nephews, entirely, elephants, friend, friendlier, friendliest, friendliness, weathered, breakfasts, breakfasted, breakfasting, liberties, liberate, visitors, visit, visits, visited, visiting, wild, wildness, withdraws, withdrew, withdrawing, industries, industrial, interests, interested, interesting, installs, installed, installing, talented

127

IV

Mystery Words. A spelling word is hidden in each mystery word. Circle and write the spelling words.

a. pinephewes _____

b. entiresome _____

c. telephantom _____

d. lemonadear _____

e. offriendlying _____

f. sweathere _____

g. breakfastener _____

h. libertyphoon _____

i. visitorment _____

j. bewildernesses _____

k. withdrawers _____

l. windustrying _____

m. sprinterestone _____

n. stalentrance _____

o. rainstalled _____

V. Circles and Squares. Match the circles and squares to form words from the spelling list. Write the words.

1. _____

2. _____

3. _____

4. _____

5. _____

Spelling Words

nephew everywhere entire elephant lemonade anyhow anyone anywhere anyway friendly weather breakfast liberty visitor wilderness withdraw industry interest install talent

VI. Guide Words. These word pairs are guide words from the **Glossary/SPELLEX®**. Write the words from the spelling list that appear on the same page as each pair of guide words.

act—apartment

1. _____
2. _____
3. _____
4. _____

bought—canyon

5. _____

dry—escape

6. _____
7. _____

everywhere—festive

8. _____

freeze—graze

9. _____

help—ironing

10. _____
11. _____
12. _____

known—machine

13. _____
14. _____

mud—offer

15. _____

stray—talent

16. _____

uncle—west

17. _____
18. _____

western—wrist

19. _____
20. _____

VII. Word Detective. The same two letters are missing from each of the words below. Write the words.

a. _____

b. _____

c. _____

d. _____

e. _____

f. _____

g. _____

h. _____

	n	t	e		e	s	t	
	v	i	s		t	o		
	l		b	e		t	y	
	e	n	t			e		
	f			e	n	d	l	y
w		l	d	e		n	e	s	s
	n	d	u	s	t		y	
	w		t	h	d		a	w

VIII. Generally Speaking. Write a spelling word in the group it best fits.

a. lion, tiger, _____

b. ability, skill, _____

c. rain, snow, _____

d. _____ , lunch, dinner

e. set, adjust, _____

f. uncle, niece, _____

g. punch, juice, _____

IX. All in a Sentence. Use each of the spelling words in sentences about one of the following titles. Use as many **Other Word Forms** (p. 127) as you can. Circle the spelling words and the other word forms you used.

<u>The Winter Camp Trip</u> or <u>The Substitute Teacher</u>

Example: *It is no fun to camp* (anywhere) *with* (anyone) *in bad* (weather) *.*

X. Final Test. Write each spelling word.

130

Lesson 33

I. Check Test. Write each spelling word.

II. Spelling Words and Phrases

scar	will leave a **scar**
scarf	tightened my **scarf**
guard	the **guard** at the gate
charge	to **charge** forward
largely	**largely** to blame
carpet	sat on the **carpet**
darkness	the **darkness** of night
pardon	to beg your **pardon**
harvest	completed the **harvest**
harbor	headed for the **harbor**
artist	the **artist** at work
parties	some birthday **parties**
partner	worked with a **partner**
hardware	at the **hardware** store
carloads	**carloads** of spectators
alarm	sounded the **alarm**
apartment	a five-room **apartment**
depart	will **depart** on schedule
remarkable	a **remarkable** stunt
parents	for our **parents**

III. Find a Fit. Write each word in its correct shape.

a.
b.
c.
d.
e.
f.
g.
h.
i.
j.
k.
l.
m.
n.
o.
p.
q.
r.
s.
t.

Other Word Forms
scars, scarred, scarring, scarves,
guarded, charges, charged, charging,
large, larger, largest, carpeted,
carpeting, dark, darkest, darkening,
pardoned, pardonable, harvester,
harvesting, harboring, harbored, artists,
artistic, art, party, partnership,
hardwares, carload, alarmed, alarming,
apartments, departs, departing,
departure, remark, remarked, parent,
parental

131

IV. Little Word—Big Word. Write the big word or words from the spelling list that include each little word below.

a. You find a <u>part</u> in _____ , _____ , _____ ,

and _____ .

b. See the <u>car</u> in _____ , _____ , _____ ,

and _____ .

c. You find <u>hard</u> in _____ .

d. There is an <u>arm</u> in _____ .

e. You find <u>rents</u> in _____ .

f. See the <u>or</u> in _____ .

g. There is a <u>vest</u> in _____ .

h. You find a <u>mark</u> in _____ .

i. There is <u>dark</u> in _____ .

j. You find <u>large</u> in _____ .

V. Bases and Suffixes. The spelling list contains thirteen base words and seven words with suffixes. Write each spelling word.

Words With Suffixes	Base Words	Words With Suffixes	Base Words
a. partnership	_____	k. pardonable	_____
b. hardwares	_____	l. scarred	_____
c. alarming	_____	m. scarves	_____
d. apartments	_____	n. _____ remark	
e. departing	_____	o. _____ parent	
f. harvesting	_____	p. _____ carload	
g. harbored	_____	q. _____ art	
h. guarded	_____	r. _____ party	
i. charging	_____	s. _____ large	
j. carpeted	_____	t. _____ dark	

Spelling Words

scar scarf guard charge largely carpet darkness
pardon harvest harbor artist parties partner hardware
carloads alarm apartment depart remarkable parents

VI. Word Parts. Answer each question with an <u>ar</u> word from the spelling list.

a. What <u>ar</u> likes to paint? _____

b. What <u>ar</u> will leave? _____

c. What <u>ar</u> needs someone else? _____

d. What <u>ar</u> happens on birthdays? _____

e. What <u>ar</u> is a place to live? _____

f. What <u>ar</u> is nails and tools? _____

g. What <u>ar</u> excuses someone? _____

h. What <u>ar</u> rings a warning? _____

i. What <u>ar</u> provides protection? _____

j. What <u>ar</u> is not light? _____

k. What <u>ar</u> happens mostly? _____

l. What <u>ar</u> means you will pay later? _____

m. What <u>ar</u> is usually done in the fall? _____

n. What <u>ar</u> is found underfoot? _____

o. What <u>ar</u> is a safe home for your boat? _____

p. What <u>ar</u> keeps your neck warm? _____

q. What <u>ar</u> feeds you and cares for you? _____

r. What <u>ar</u> is amazing? _____

s. What <u>ar</u> was a wound? _____

t. What <u>ar</u> fills automobiles? _____

VII. Guide Words. These word pairs are guide words from the Glossary/SPELLEX®. Write the words from the spelling list that appear on the same page as each pair of guide words.

act—apartment

1. _____
2. _____

appoint—bait

3. _____

captain—chosen

4. _____
5. _____
6. _____

copy—daughter

7. _____

day—dropped

8. _____

great—helmet

9. _____
10. _____
11. _____
12. _____

known—machine

13. _____

often—pasture

14. _____
15. _____
16. _____
17. _____

quarter—replied

18. _____

reply—scarf

19. _____
20. _____

VIII. Book List. Using all of the spelling words, make up titles and authors for books. You may use **Other Word Forms** (p. 131). Circle the spelling words and the other word forms you used.

IX. Final Test. Write each spelling word.

134

Lesson 34

I. Check Test. Write each spelling word.

II. Spelling Words and Phrases

schoolmate	introducing a **schoolmate**
rooster	when the **rooster** overslept
proving	**proving** you to be correct
improved	**improved** quickly
whose	**whose** lost kitten
due	if the book is **due**
duties	**duties** of the principal
rulers	metal **rulers**
student	elected the **student**
truth	to tell the **truth**
suits	wet bathing **suits**
ruin	will **ruin** the story
groups	several **groups**
route	changed their **route**
flew	**flew** south for the winter
blew	**blew** up the balloons
chewing	**chewing** the gum
threw	**threw** it to the ground
newspapers	has read two **newspapers**
sew	will **sew** on a patch

III. Find a Fit. Write each word in its correct shape.

a.
b.
c.
d.
e.
f.
g.
h.
i.
j.
k.
l.
m.
n.
o.
p.
q.
r.
s.
t.

Other Word Forms

schoolmates, roosters, prove, proved, proof, improve, improving, improvement, who, whom, dues, duty, dutiful, dutifully, rule, rules, ruled, ruler, students, truths, truthful, suit, suited, ruined, ruining, group, grouped, grouping, routed, routing, fly, flies, flying, blow, blows, blowing, chew, chews, chewed, throw, throwing, thrown, newspaper, sewn, sewed

IV. Break the Code.
Use the code to write the spelling words. Next to each spelling word, write an **Other Word Form** (p. 135).

a	b	c	d	e	f	g	h	i	j	k	l	m	n	o	p	q	r	s	t	u	v	w	x	y	z
↓	↓	↓	↓	↓	↓	↓	↓	↓	↓	↓	↓	↓	↓	↓	↓	↓	↓	↓	↓	↓	↓	↓	↓	↓	↓
g	d	j	r	u	e	y	w	k	a	c	p	s	h	b	n	l	m	f	o	t	x	z	v	q	i

a. hntmf _____ _____

b. mfh _____ _____

c. deqfdm _____ _____

d. undfh _____ _____

e. knfhzpa _____ _____

f. oqfh _____ _____

g. pfhmljlfdm _____ _____

h. dttmufd _____ _____

i. mknttqrjuf _____ _____

j. ldtxzpa _____ _____

k. sqfh _____ _____

l. zrldtxfb _____ _____

m. udeun _____ _____

n. beuzfm _____ _____

o. muebfpu _____ _____

p. adtelm _____ _____

q. dteuf _____ _____

r. dezp _____ _____

s. mezum _____ _____

t. bef _____ _____

V. Homophones.
Write the spelling word or **Other Word Form** (p. 135) that is a homophone for each word below.

a. so _____   e. root _____

b. through _____   f. dew _____

c. blue _____   g. choose _____

d. flue _____

Spelling Words

schoolmate rooster proving improved whose due
duties rulers student truth suits ruin groups
route flew blew chewing threw newspapers sew

VI. Crossword Puzzle. Solve the puzzle by using all the words from the spelling list. Check your answers in the **Glossary/SPELLEX®**.

Across

6. a pal in your class
7. did to put out candles
9. to wreck
10. to connect with thread
11. did to a ball
15. a male chicken
16. responsibilities
17. the road to take
18. how birds got south

Down

1. showing to be true
2. crushing with teeth
3. possessive of *who*
4. did better
5. reading materials printed daily
6. a learner in school
8. several sets of people
12. kings
13. a true statement
14. sets of clothing
16. expected

VII. Scrambled Words. Unscramble the scrambled word to find the spelling word that completes the sentence. Write the word.

Scrambled Words

a. Two _____ of players entered the arena.   ogrups

b. The archeologists carefully examined the _____ .   unir

c. You have really _____ your grades in science.   dprimove

d. Sometimes _____ is stranger than fiction.   thutr

e. Use these _____ for measuring.   rsleru

f. The _____ crowed in the barnyard.   steroor

g. The lawyer is _____ their innocence.   ingvpro

h. Every _____ passed the test.   ntusted

i. _____ shoes are these?   swhoe

j. The tailor pressed the _____ .   stuis

VIII. Guide Words. These word pairs are guide words from the **Glossary/SPELLEX®**. Write the words from the spelling list that appear on the same page as each pair of guide words.

balloon—bottom

1. _____

captain—chosen

2. _____

dry—escape

3. _____

4. _____

5. _____

fifteen—freedom

6. _____

great—helmet

7. _____

help—ironing

8. _____

mud—offer

9. _____

president—quart

10. _____

reply—scarf

11. _____

12. _____

13. _____

14. _____

schoolmate—skinned

15. _____

16. _____

stray—talent

17. _____

18. _____

taught—ugly

19. _____

western—wrist

20. _____

IX. Final Test. Write each spelling word.

138

Lesson 35

I. Check Test. Write each spelling word.

II. Spelling Words and Phrases

beautiful	a **beautiful** city
musician	a lonely **musician**
fir	a forest of **fir** trees
skirt	a **skirt** and sweater
circle	joined the **circle**
squirrel	a chipmunk or a **squirrel**
concern	had no **concern**
connect	to **connect** the wires
congress	a **congress** of delegates
doctor	called the **doctor**
beyond	**beyond** their control
closet	locked in the **closet**
promise	kept their **promise**
costume	will put on the **costume**
products	several new **products**
probably	**probably** will win
popular	not a **popular** idea
horizontal	onto the **horizontal** bar
electricity	the hum of **electricity**
addition	in **addition** to

III. Find a Fit. Write each word in its correct shape.

a.
b.
c.
d.
e.
f.
g.
h.
i.
j.
k.
l.
m.
n.
o.
p.
q.
r.
s.
t.

Other Word Forms
beautifully, beauty, music, musical, musically, firs, skirted, skirting, circled, circling, squirrels, concerned, concerning, connector, connects, congresses, congressional, doctoring, closets, promises, promised, promising, costumed, production, produce, produces, produced, producing, probable, probability, popularly, popularity, horizontally, electric, electrify, electrician, additional, additionally

IV. Break the Code. Use the code to write the spelling words.

a	b	c	d	e	f	g	h	i	j	k	l	m
↕	↕	↕	↕	↕	↕	↕	↕	↕	↕	↕	↕	↕
z	y	x	w	v	u	t	s	r	q	p	o	n

a. xlmxvim   _concern_

b. xlmtivhh   _congress_

c. zwwrgrlm   _addition_

d. yvzfgrufo   _beautiful_

e. vovxgirxrgb   _electricity_

f. yvblmw   _beyond_

g. uri   _fir_

h. hprig   _skirt_

i. klkfozi   _popular_

j. nfhrxrzm   _musician_

k. xrixov   _circle_

l. xolhvg   _closet_

m. xlhgfnv   _costume_

n. sliralmgzo   _horizontal_

o. kilnrhv   _promise_

p. kilwfxgh   _products_

q. kilyzyob   _probably_

r. hjfriivo   _squirrel_

s. wlxgli   _doctor_

t. xlmmvxg   _connect_

V. Not _____ , But. Use each of the spelling words in one of the phrases below.

a. not solar power, but _____

b. not a chipmunk, but a _____

c. not quotients, but _____

d. not underline, but _____

e. not a painter, but a _____

f. not a cupboard, but a _____

g. not a usual outfit, but a _____

h. not subtraction, but _____

i. not impossibly, but _____

j. not unfavorable, but _____

k. not a senate, but a _____

l. not ugly, but _____

m. not pants, but a _____

n. not beside, but _____

o. not unhitch, but _____

p. not a secret, but a _____

q. not vertical, but _____

r. not a nurse, but a _____

s. not an elm, but a _____

t. not disinterest, but _____

Spelling Words

beautiful musician fir skirt circle squirrel concern
connect congress doctor beyond closet promise costume
products probably popular horizontal electricity addition

VI. Private Eye. Search the spelling list to solve each clue.

a. She works in a hospital.   _____

b. You'll find clothing stored here.   _____

c. It likes acorns.   _____

d. This is not vertical.   _____

e. Most stage actors wear one.   _____

f. A kilt is similar to this.   _____

g. A violinist is certainly one.   _____

h. Sometimes this can be shocking.   _____

i. This can never be square.   _____

j. Representatives and senators form this.   _____

k. The spruce is definitely one.   _____

l. Math students do well at this.   _____

m. A vow is one that can't be broken.   _____

n. Bridges do this very well.   _____

o. This is outside the limits.   _____

p. This is most likely.   _____

q. Successful rock groups are always so.   _____

r. These are answers in multiplication.   _____

s. Magnificent sunsets are always this.   _____

t. If you worry, you have lots of this.   _____

VII. Guide Words. These word pairs are guide words from the
Glossary/SPELLEX®. Write the words from the spelling list
that appear on the same page as each pair of guide words.

act—apartment	copy—daughter	mud—offer
1. _____	9. _____	14. _____

balloon—bottom	day—dropped	patch—preparing
2. _____	10. _____	15. _____
3. _____		

circle—copper	dry—escape	president—quart
4. _____	11. _____	16. _____
5. _____	fifteen—freedom	17. _____
6. _____	12. _____	18. _____
7. _____		
8. _____	help-ironing	skirt—strain
	13. _____	19. _____
		20. _____

VIII. All in a Sentence. Write all of the spelling words in sentences. Use as many
Other Word Forms (p. 139) as you can. Circle the spelling words and the other
word forms you used.

Example: *The* (costumes) *were* (beautifully) *made.*

IX. Final Test. Write each spelling word.

142

1	2	3	4	5
gravel	gathering	practicing	shadow	captain
visitor	interest	elephant	talent	breakfast
scar	pardon	harvest	alarm	remarkable
ruin	proving	improved	rulers	sew
skirt	connect	concern	promise	circle

I. Word Building. Add word parts to each spelling word or its base word to make other word forms. If you need help , use the **Glossary/SPELLEX®**.

Spelling Words	*s*	*ed*	*ing*
Example: walked	*walks*		*walking*
a. practicing			
b. proving			
c. ruin			
d. visitor			
e. pardon			
f. improved			
g. alarm			
h. breakfast			
i. shadow			
j. interest			
k. promise			
l. captain			
m. sew			
n. elephant			
o. talent			
p. gravel			
q. remarkable			
r. rulers			
s. concern			
t. connect			
u. harvest			
v. skirt			
w. scar			
x. circle			
y. gathering			

36

1	2	3	4	5
altogether	palace	piano	pajamas	handful
wilderness	lemonade	friendly	nephew	install
apartment	parties	carpet	scarf	guard
groups	due	whose	blew	chewing
beautiful	beyond	probably	costume	squirrel

II. Puzzling Clues. Use other word forms or the spelling words to complete each clue. The number below each group of spaces tells you in what column you can find the spelling word. Use each word or its other word form only once.

a. Never incompletely — — — — — — — — — —
  1

b. Its opposite is never "palmore." — — — — — — — — — —
  3

c. Putting in the telephone lines — — — — — — — — — —
  5

d. Furry nut gatherers — — — — — — — —
  5

e. Its opposite is never "feetfuls." — — — — — — — —
  5

f. Clothing for trick-or-treaters — — — — — — — —
  4

g. A summertime pick-me-up — — — — — — — —
  2

h. Nieces are never these. — — — — — — —
  4

i. People walk all over them. — — — — — — —
  3

j. Small blankets for the neck — — — — — — —
  4

k. Homes for queens and kings — — — — — — —
  2

l. Night clothing — — — — — — —
  4

m. Their keys fit no locks. — — — — — —
  3

n. They keep an eye on things. — — — — — —
  5

o. Far out! — — — — — —
  2

p. What the north wind does — — — — —
  4

q. Describes some animals and some playing cards — — — —
  1

r. Your teeth do this best. — — — —
  5

s. Describes what your library books could be — — —
  2

t. The mystery person? — — —
  3

144

1	2	3	4	5	36
afterward	charge	factory	horizontal	products	
anyhow	congress	flew	musician	rooster	
anyone	depart	grandfather	parents	schoolmate	
anyway	duty	harbor	plastic	tablet	
anywhere	everywhere	hardware	popular	threw	

III. Before and After.

a. Find the spelling word that comes alphabetically right *before* each word below. Write the spelling word and an other word form for each spelling word. If you need help, use the **Glossary/SPELLEX®**.

Before	Spelling Words	Other Word Forms
1. aim	—— —— —— —— —— —— —— —— ——	_____
2. rough	—— —— —— —— —— —— ——	_____
3. harvest	—— —— —— —— —— —— —— ——	_____
4. grape	—— —— —— —— —— —— —— —— —— ——	_____
5. cheat	—— —— —— —— —— —— ——	_____
6. flight	—— —— —— ——	_____
7. tackle	—— —— —— —— —— ——	_____
8. hose	—— —— —— —— —— —— —— —— —— ——	_____
9. score	—— —— —— —— —— —— —— ——	_____
10. thrill	—— —— —— —— ——	_____
11. depend	—— —— —— —— —— ——	_____

b. Now find the spelling word that comes alphabetically right *after* each word below. Write the spelling word and an other word form for each spelling word.

After	Spelling Words	Other Word Forms
1. conduct	—— —— —— —— —— —— —— ——	_____
2. duties	—— —— —— ——	_____
3. parent	—— —— —— —— —— —— ——	_____
4. handsome	—— —— —— —— —— ——	_____
5. product	—— —— —— —— —— —— —— ——	_____
6. platform	—— —— —— —— —— —— ——	_____
7. fact	—— —— —— —— —— —— ——	_____
8. music	—— —— —— —— —— —— —— ——	_____
9. plantation	—— —— —— —— —— —— ——	_____

c. Write the five words that appear in the spelling list but have no other word forms. _____ _____ _____

_____ _____

36

1	2	3	4	5
avenue	weather	handsome	families	pasture
industry	entire	although	liberty	withdraw
largely	darkness	artist	carloads	partner
newspapers	route	suits	student	duties
fir	doctor	closet	electricity	addition

IV. S-t-r-e-t-c-h the Meaning. Write other word forms or the spelling words to stretch the words and their meanings. The number tells you in what column you can find the spelling word. Write each word or its other word form only once. If you need help, use the **Glossary/SPELLEX®**.

a. _____ : places where shirts and _____ hang
   3   3

b. _____ : persons sometimes thought of as _____
   2   3
   in the operating room

c. _____ : _____ for city drivers
   1   2

d. daily _____ : important products of printing _____
         1   1

e. _____ trees: evergreens often found in very _____
   1   1
   forests

f. _____ : describes autos stuffed with _____ members
   4   4

g. _____ : places where cows graze
   5

h. _____ bulbs: things that bring light to _____ places
   4   2

i. _____ : a freedom that is everyone's _____ to
   4   5
   keep alive

j. your _____ : persons who often think they are the _____
        5   3
   members of the team

k. total: the _____ amount in _____
              2   5

l. fewer _____ : what results when some classmates are
         4
   _____ from your group
   5

m. fair _____ : a time for a picnic, _____ there could be
        2   3
   some rain

146

SPELLEX® Glossary
Level E

This section of your spelling book is called **SPELLEX® Glossary—Level E.** It is a collection of the spelling words from **Working Words in Spelling—Level E,** together with the phonetic spelling, part of speech, definition, sample phrase, and other word forms for each spelling word.

The **SPELLEX® Glossary** is a useful tool for your spelling work and your everyday writing. It is a valuable resource when doing your spelling exercises and when practicing and reviewing your spelling words. From the groups of other word forms, you can choose the best words to express your ideas or to add variety and smoothness to your writing. The **SPELLEX® Glossary** gives you a quick way to check the spellings and meanings of words.

The **SPELLEX® Glossary** is arranged very simply. All the entry words are listed in alphabetical order. All the spelling words are printed in dark type. If the spelling word is not a base word, you are told what the base word is. With the base word and its definition, you will find the other word forms.

Example: help |hĕlp| *v.* To aid; do what is useful: *will help me clean the house.* **helps, helped, helping, helpful, helpfully, helpfulness, helpless**

helpful |hĕlp′fəl| *adj.* Providing aid; useful: *a helpful worker.* [see *help*]

PRONUNCIATION KEY

ă	pat	j	judge	sh	dish, ship
ā	aid, fey, pay	k	cat, kick, pique	t	tight
â	air, care, wear	l	lid, needle	th	path, thin
ä	father	m	am, man, mum	*th*	bathe, this
b	bib	n	no, sudden	ŭ	cut, rough
ch	church	ng	thing	û	circle, firm, heard,
d	deed	ŏ	horrible, pot		term, turn, urge, word
ĕ	pet, pleasure	ō	go, hoarse, row, toe	v	cave, valve, vine
ē	be, bee, easy, leisure	ô	alter, caught, for, paw	w	with
f	fast, fife, off, phase, rough	oi	boy, noise, oil	y	yes
g	gag	ou	cow, out	yōō	abuse, use
h	hat	ŏŏ	took	z	rose, size, xylophone, zebra
hw	which	ōō	boot, fruit	zh	garage, pleasure, vision
ĭ	pit	p	pop	ə	about, silent, pencil,
ī	by, guy, pie	r	roar		lemon, circus
î	dear, deer, fierce, mere	s	miss, sauce, see	ər	butter

STRESS
Primary stress ′   **bi·ol′o·gy** |bī ŏl′ə jē| Secondary stress ′   **bi′o·log′i·cal** |bī′ə lŏj′ĭ kəl|

A

act |ăkt| n. One of the main divisions of a play or opera: *a long first act.* **acts, acted, acting, action, actor, actress**

acts |ăkts| n. More than one act: *a play with three acts.* [see *act*]

add |ăd| v. To find the sum of two or more numbers: *will add these numbers.* **adds, added, adding, addition, additions, additional, additionally**

addition |ə dĭsh'ən| n. The adding of two or more numbers: *correct addition.* —**In addition to**— Besides. [see *add*]

afterward |ăf'tər wərd| adv. Later: *will sign up afterward.* **afterwards**

aim |ām| n. **1.** The act of pointing something, usually a weapon, at an object: *took aim at the target.* **2.** A purpose or goal: *the aim of the meeting.* **aims, aimed, aiming, aimless, aimlessly, aimlessness**

alarm |ə lärm'| n. A device that, when sounded, warns people: *a burglar alarm.* **alarms, alarmed, alarming, alarmingly**

allow |ə lou'| v. To let happen or be done: *will allow them to play.* **allows, allowed, allowing, allowable, allowance**

all right |ôl'rīt'| Correct: *if the answers were all right.*

alter |ôl'tər| v. **1.** To change in some way: *will alter her way of dressing.* **2.** To change the fit of clothing: *to alter the hem on a skirt.* **alters, altered, altering, alteration**

altered |ôl'tərd| v. **1.** Changed in some way: *altered the schedule.* **2.** Changed the fit of clothing: *altered the coat sleeves.* [see *alter*]

although |ôl thō'| conj. Even though: *although you helped.*

altogether |ôl'tə gĕth'ər| adv. Completely; totally: *altogether pleased with the results.*

America |ə měr'ĭ kə| n. The United States: *born in America.* **Americas, American, Americans, Americanize, Americanism**

American |ə měr'ĭ kən| adj. Of the United States: *American cities.* n. A citizen of the United States: *an American living in Europe.* [see *America*]

amuse |ə myōōz'| v. To give pleasure by making someone laugh or smile: *will amuse us with jokes.* **amuses, amused, amusing, amusingly, amusement**

anger |ăng'gər| n. A feeling of rage against someone or something that has caused injury or wrong: *a shout of anger.* **angers, angered, angering, angry, angrier, angriest, angrily**

angle |ăng'gəl| n. The space formed between two straight lines when they meet: *the angle formed by the hands of a clock.* **angles, angled, angling**

angry |ăng'grē| adj. Feeling or showing anger: *in an angry mood.* [see *anger*]

ankle |ăng'kəl| n. The joint attaching the foot to the rest of the leg: *sprained her ankle.* **ankles**

answer |ăn'sər| v. To respond to a question: *to answer correctly.* **answers, answered, answering**

anyhow |ĕn'ē hou'| adv. In any case; nevertheless: *will worry anyhow.*

anyone |ĕn'ē wŭn'| pron. Any person; anybody: *if anyone knows.*

anyway |ĕn'ē wā'| adv. In any case: *will rain anyway.*

anywhere |ĕn'ē hwâr'| adv. At, in, or to any place: *will go anywhere in the United States.*

apartment |ə pärt'mənt| n. A room or group of rooms rented as a home: *the apartment on the fifth floor.* **apartments**

ă pat / ā pay / â care / ä father / ĕ pet / ē be / ĭ pit / ī pie / î fierce / ŏ pot / ō go / ô paw, for / oi oil / ōō book / ōō boot / ou out / ŭ cut / û fur / th the / th thin / hw which / zh vision / ə ago, item, pencil, atom, circus
©1977 by Houghton Mifflin Company. Reprinted by permission from THE AMERICAN HERITAGE SCHOOL DICTIONARY.

appoint |ə **point'**| v. To select a time or place: *to appoint the gym for the school fair.* **appoints, appointed, appointing, appointment, appointments**

appointment |ə **point'**mənt| n. A prearranged meeting: *an appointment at three o'clock.* [see *appoint*]

April |ā'prəl| adj. Of April: *April flowers.* n. The fourth month of the year: *a birthday in April.* **Apr.**

apron |a'prən| n. A garment tied around the waist to protect the clothes on the front of the body: *an apron worn to do dishes.* **aprons, aproned**

aren't |ärnt| Contraction for *are not: because we aren't going.*

arrow |ăr'ō| n. A thin, pointed shaft that is shot from a bow: *bow and arrow.* **arrows**

art |ärt| n. Drawing, painting, and sculpture: *courses in art and poetry.* **arts, artist, artists, artistic, artistically, artistry**

artist |är'tĭst| n. A person who draws, paints, or sculpts: *the artist who is carving the sculpture.* [see *art*]

ash |ăsh| n. The remains of something that has been completely burned: *ash in the fireplace.* **ashes, ashy**

ashamed |ə shāmd'| adj. Feeling uncomfortable for having done something wrong: *ashamed of his actions.* [see *shame*]

ashes |ăsh'ĭz| n. The remains of something that has been completely burned: *swept the ashes.* [see *ash*]

astronaut |ăs' trə nôt'| n. A member of the crew of a spacecraft: *the astronaut in the control room.* **astronauts, astronautic, astronautics, astronautical**

attach |ə tăch'| v. To join together: *will attach the jigsaw pieces to one another.* **attaches, attached, attaching, attachable, attachment**

attached |ə tăcht'| v. Joined together: *attached the hook to the fishing rod.* [see *attach*]

attack |ə tăk'| n. The act of using force or weapons against: *a surprise attack.* v. To begin a fight: *to attack without warning.* **attacks, attacked, attacking, attacker**

attend |ə tĕnd'| v. To go to; be present at: *will attend the party.* **attends, attended, attending, attendance, attendant**

audience |ô'dē əns| n. The people gathered to see or hear something: *large audience in the theater.* **audiences**

August |ô'gəst| adj. Of August: *August weather.* n. The eighth month of the year: *the first week in August.* **Aug.**

aunt |ănt| n. The sister of one's mother or father: *my father's aunt.* **aunts**

automobile |ô'tə mə bēl'| n. A passenger vehicle with an engine, driven on land: *an automobile with front-wheel drive.* **automobiles, auto**

autumn |ô'təm| adj. Related to autumn: *autumn harvest.* n. The season between summer and winter: *a rainy autumn.* **autumns, autumnal**

avenue |ăv'ə nōō'| n. A wide street: *cars along the avenue.* **avenues, Ave.**

average |ăv'ər ĭj| n. The number that is typical or representative of a group of numbers: *because 25 is the average of 20 and 30.* adj. Usual: *an average amount of rain in the month of September.* **averages, averaged, averaging**

awful |ô'fəl| adj. Terrible: *awful temper.* **awfully**

B

bad |băd| adj. Not good: *bad behavior.* **worse, worst**

badge |băj| n. Something worn to show rank, membership, occupation, etc.: *the officer's badge.* **badges**

bait |bāt| n. Anything used to attract animals or fish to be caught: *bait for trout.* **baits, baited, baiting**

balloon |bə lōōn'| *n.* An elastic rubber bag made to be filled with air or other gases: *bought a balloon at the parade.* **balloons, ballooned, ballooning**

bare |bâr| *adj.* Unclothed: *bare shoulders.* **bares, bared, baring, barer, barest, barely**

barrel |bâr'əl| *n.* A large wooden container with round, flat ends and sides that curve out: *a barrel for water.* **barrels, barreled, barreling, barrelful**

basement |bās'mənt| *n.* The lowest story of a building, usually below ground: *boxes in the basement.* **basements**

beam |bēm| *n.* A ray of light: *the beam from the lighthouse.* **beams, beamed, beaming**

beat |bēt| *v.* **1.** To cause to lose: *will beat him at checkers.* **2.** To mix by stirring quickly: *will beat the egg whites.* **beats, beaten, beating, beater**

beaten |bēt'n| *adj.* **1.** Defeated: *the beaten enemy.* **2.** Mixed by stirring quickly: *has beaten the cake batter.* [see *beat*]

beautiful |byōō'tə fəl| *adj.* Pleasing to the senses: *a beautiful painting.* [see *beauty*]

beauty |byōō'tē| *n.* A quality that pleases the senses: *the beauty of music.* **beautiful, beautifully, beautify, beautified, beautifying, beautification**

beg |bĕg| *v.* To plead; ask for earnestly: *to beg forgiveness.* **begs, begged, begging, beggar**

begged |bĕgd| *v.* Pleaded; asked for earnestly: *begged for some help.* [see *beg*]

begin |bĭ gĭn'| *v.* To start: *will begin the puzzle.* **begins, began, begun, beginning**

beginning |bĭ gĭn'ĭng| *v.* Starting: *beginning to heal.* [see *begin*]

betray |bĭ trā'| *v.* To be a traitor to; double-cross: *to betray the soldiers to the enemy.* **betrays, betrayed, betraying, betrayer, betrayal**

beyond |bē ŏnd'| *prep.* Outside the reach or understanding of: *beyond my ability.*

bitter |bĭt'ər| *adj.* Sharp or unpleasant in flavor: *the bitter fruit.* **bitterly, bitterness**

bleed |blēd| *v.* To lose blood: *did bleed from the wound.* **bleeds, bled, bleeding, blood, bloody, bloodier, bloodiest, bloodiness**

bleeding |blē'dĭng| *n.* The losing of blood: *slow bleeding from the cut.* [see *bleed*]

blew |blōō| *v.* Sent out a strong current of air: *blew on the hot soup.* [see *blow*]

blood |blŭd| *n.* The red fluid that moves through the body, carrying oxygen, digested food, and waste: *blood from a vein.* [see *bleed*]

blossom |blŏs'əm| *n.* A flower: *the blossom on the plant.* **blossoms, blossomed, blossoming, blossomless**

blouse |blous| *n.* A loose shirt worn by women: *cotton blouse.* **blouses, bloused**

blow |blō| *v.* To send out a strong current of air: *to blow air into the balloon.* **—Blow up—** To fill with air. **blows, blew, blown, blowing, blower**

bodies |bŏd'ēz| *n.* More than one body: *heavenly bodies of stars.* [see *body*]

body |bŏd'ē| *n.* A mass or portion of matter: *body of water.* **bodies, bodily**

bond |bŏnd| *n.* Something that ties or unites: *a bond between sisters.* **bonds, bonded, bonding, bondage**

border |bôr'dər| *n.* An outer part or edge of anything: *the county border.* **borders, bordered, bordering**

bore |bôr| *v.* **1.** To make a hole by using a tool that turns: *will bore through the wall.* **2.** To make weary by being dull or uninteresting: *movies that bore me.* **bores, bored, boring, boredom, borer**

bottom |bŏt'əm| *n.* The lowest part or edge: *at the bottom of the box.* **bottoms, bottomless**

ă **pat** / ā **pay** / â **care** / ä **father** / ĕ **pet** / ē **be** / ĭ **pit** / ī **pie** / î **fierce** / ŏ **pot** / ō **go** / ô **paw, for** / oi **oil** / ōō **book** / ōō **boot** / ou **out** / ŭ **cut** / û **fur** / *th* **the** / th **thin** / hw **which** / zh **vision** / ə **ago, item, pencil, atom, circus**

bought |bôt| *v.* Purchased: *bought new shoes.* [see *buy*]

braid |brād| *n.* A length of three or more strands of ribbon or hair woven together: *long blond braid. v.* To weave three or more strands together: *will braid her hair.* **braids, braided, braiding**

brain |brān| *n.* The part of the central nervous system in vertebrates that is enclosed in the skull and consists of nerve cells and fibers for controlling almost all bodily functions: *X ray of the brain.* **brains, brainy, brainier, brainiest, brainless**

brake |brāk| *n.* Something used to slow down or stop the motion of a wheeled vehicle by rubbing against or pressing: *the brake on the bicycle.* **brakes, braked, braking**

branch |brănch| *n.* Any wood part growing out from the trunk of a tree: *a fallen tree branch.* **branches, branched, branching**

branches |brăn′chĭz| *n.* More than one branch: *large branches of a redwood.* [see *branch*]

brass |brăs| *n.* An alloy that contains mainly copper and zinc: *polished the brass.* **brasses, brassy**

break |brāk| *v.* To come apart by force: *will break on the tile floor. n.* A brief interruption in work: *a morning break.* **breaks, broke, breaking, broken, breakable**

breakfast |brĕk′fəst| *n.* The first meal of the day: *eggs for breakfast.* **breakfasts, breakfasted, breakfasting**

bridge |brĭj| *n.* A structure that provides a way over a river, road, or other obstacle: *steel bridge.* **bridges, bridged, bridging**

bring |brĭng| *v.* To come with someone or something: *will bring a guest.* **brings, brought, bringing**

brook |brŏok| *n.* A small natural stream of water: *fishing in the brook.* **brooks**

brought |brôt| *v.* Came with someone or something: *brought a gift for you.* [see *bring*]

build |bĭld| *v.* To make or construct by putting materials or parts together: *will build a house.* **builds, built, building, buildings, builder**

building |bĭl′dĭng| *adj.* Related to building: *the building renovation. n.* A structure like a house or store; something built: *brick building. v.* Making or constructing: *building a garage.* [see *build*]

bundle |bŭn′dl| *n.* Several things tied or wrapped together: *a bundle of old clothes.* **bundles, bundled, bundling, bundler**

burglar |bûr′glər| *n.* A person who breaks into a building to steal: *arrested the burglar inside the bank.* **burglars, burglary, burglarize, burglarized**

burst |bûrst| *v.* To go, come, or do suddenly or by force: *as water burst from the hose.* **bursts, bursting**

button |bŭt′n| *n.* A disk of plastic, metal, etc., sewn on garments to hold them together or to decorate them: *a button on the cuff.* **buttons, buttoned, buttoning**

buy |bī| *v.* To get something by paying money: *will buy milk.* **buys, bought, buying, buyer**

C

cabbage |kăb′ĭj| *n.* A vegetable with leaves that overlap to form a round head: *soup made from cabbage.* **cabbages**

calf |kăf| *n.* A young cow or bull: *a calf in the barn.* **calves**

calm |käm| *adj.* Quiet or still: *was in a calm mood.* **calms, calmed, calming, calmer, calmest, calmly, calmness**

calves |kăvz| *n.* More than one calf: *two calves in the pasture.* [see *calf*]

canal |kə năl′| *n.* A waterway dug for irrigation or navigation: *digging a canal.* **canals**

canyon |kăn′yən| *n.* A deep hollow in the earth's surface, carved by a river: *the steep walls of the canyon.* **canyons**

captain |kăp'tən| *n.* The leader of a group: *captain of the team.* **captains, captained, captaining, captainship**

carload |kär'lōd'| *n.* As much as a car can hold: *carload of groceries.* **carloads**

carloads |kär'lōdz'| *n.* More than one carload: *carloads of students.* [see *carload*]

carpet |kär'pĭt| *n.* A woven covering for floors: *worn gray carpet.* **carpets, carpeted, carpeting**

carried |kăr'ēd| *v.* Taken from one place to another: *was carried on his back.* [see *carry*]

carries |kăr'ēz| *v.* Takes something from one place to another: *carries the small packages.* [see *carry*]

carry |kăr'ē| *v.* To take something from one place to another: *will carry the boxes to the attic.* **carries, carried, carrying, carrier, carriage**

castle |kăs'əl| *n.* A large building or group of buildings with thick walls and other protections against attack; fort: *built a sand castle.* **castles**

catch |kăch| *v.* **1.** To become sick with: *to catch the flu.* **2.** To capture or seize: *to catch the prisoner.* **3.** To grab hold of something moving: *to catch a ball.* **catches, caught, catching, catcher, catchers**

catcher |kăch'ər| *n.* The player behind home plate who catches the ball from the pitcher: *the foul ball caught by the catcher.* [see *catch*]

caught |kôt| *v.* **1.** Became sick with: *caught the measles.* **2.** Captured or seized: *caught the thief.* [see *catch*]

cause |kôz| *v.* To make happen: *to cause the vase to break.* **causes, caused, causing, causable**

caused |kôzd| *v.* Made happen: *caused the bad weather.* [see *cause*]

cellar |sĕl'ər| *n.* An underground room used for storage: *firewood in the cellar.* **cellars**

change |chānj| *v.* To substitute or make different: *to change the record.* **changes, changed, changing, changeable, changeably, changeless, changer**

changing |chānj'ĭng| *v.* Substituting or making different: *is changing the sheets on the bed.* [see *change*]

charge |chärj| *v.* **1.** To rush ahead: *to charge up the hill.* **2.** To delay payment by recording the amount owed: *will charge the coat.* **charges, charged, charging, charger, chargeable**

cheat |chēt| *n.* A dishonest person who tricks others: *found him to be a cheat.* **cheats, cheated, cheating, cheater**

cherries |chĕr'ēz| *n.* More than one cherry: *a bowl of cherries.* [see *cherry*]

cherry |chĕr'ē| *n.* A small, round fruit with a pit: *one cherry in the bowl.* **cherries**

chew |chōō| *v.* To grind or crush with the teeth: *will chew slowly.* **chews, chewed, chewing, chewy, chewier, chewiest, chewer**

chewing |chōō'ĭng| *v.* Grinding or crushing with the teeth: *chewing on a piece of string.* [see *chew*]

chief |chēf| *n.* The leader: *chief of police.* **chiefs, chiefly, chieftain**

chimney |chĭm'nē| *n.* A hollow, upright brick or stone structure for carrying smoke from a fireplace, furnace, etc.: *a 30-foot chimney.* **chimneys**

choice |chois| *n.* **1.** The power to choose: *no choice in the matter.* **2.** Something to be chosen among several: *choice of three colors.* **choices, choicer, choicest**

choose |chōōz| *v.* To decide or select: *to choose each piece of fruit carefully.* **chooses, chose, chosen, choosing, choosy, choice, choices**

chosen |chō'zən| *v.* Decided or selected: *had chosen the right answer.* [see *choose*]

ă pat / ā pay / â care / ä father / ĕ pet / ē be / ĭ pit / ī pie / î fierce / ŏ pot / ō go / ô paw, for / oi oil / ŏŏ book / ŏŏ boot / ou out / ŭ cut / û fur / *th* the / th thin / hw which / zh vision / ə ago, item, pencil, atom, circus
©1977 by Houghton Mifflin Company. Reprinted by permission from THE AMERICAN HERITAGE SCHOOL DICTIONARY.

circle |sûr′kəl| *n.* A closed round line whose every point is at the same distance from the center: *drew a circle. v.* To enclose in a round line: *to circle the right answer.* **circles, circled, circling, circular**

cities |sĭt′ēz| *n.* More than one city: *cities along the coast.* [see *city*]

city |sĭt′ē| *n.* A large, important town: *the city of Dallas.* **cities**

clerk |klûrk| *n.* **1.** A person who sells goods in a store: *the clerk in the shoe department.* **2.** An office worker who types, files, or keeps records: *a clerk in an insurance company.* **clerks, clerked, clerking, clerical**

cliff |klĭf| *n.* A steep face of rock: *the cliff above the valley.* **cliffs**

climate |klī′mĭt| *n.* The particular kind of weather of a place: *cold climate.* **climates, climatic**

closet |klŏz′ĭt| *n.* A small room for hanging clothes or storing supplies: *five suits in the closet.* **closets**

cloth |klôth| *n.* A material made by weaving, knitting, or matting fibers together: *wool cloth.* **cloths, clothe, clothes, clothed, clothing**

cocoa |kō′kō| *n.* A hot drink made with milk or water and the powder of cacao seeds: *cocoa on a cold day.*

collar |kŏl′ər| *n.* The part of a garment that makes a band around the neck: *a starched shirt collar.* **collars, collared, collaring**

color |kŭl′ər| *v.* To put on a shade, hue, or tint: *will color with crayons.* **colors, colored, coloring, colorful, colorfully**

colored |kŭl′ərd| *adj.* Having color, especially other than black or white: *a colored pattern.* [see *color*]

colt |kōlt| *n.* A young male horse: *colt in the barn.* **colts**

comfort |kŭm′fərt| *n.* Something or someone that gives relief from grief or fear: *the comfort of friendship. v.* To make feel better: *to comfort when sad.* **comforts, comforted, comforting, comfortable, comfortably, comfortableness, comforter**

company |kŭm′pə nē| *n.* **1.** One or more guests: *having company tonight.* **2.** A business: *the computer company.* **companies, companion**

compare |kəm pâr′| *v.* To study the similarities or differences of: *will compare their heights.* **compares, compared, comparing, comparable, comparison**

compass |kŭm′pəs| *n.* A device containing a magnetic needle, used to show geographic direction: *when the needle of the compass pointed north.* **compasses**

concern |kən sûrn′| *n.* Serious interest or worry: *a concern about her health.* **concerns, concerned, concerning**

conduct |kən dŭkt′| *v.* **1.** To direct musicians: *will conduct the choir.* **2.** To lead: *to conduct the club meeting.* **conducts, conducted, conducting, conductible, conduction, conductor**

congress |kŏng′grĭs| *n.* A meeting of representatives to discuss a subject: *a congress of doctors.* **congresses, congressional**

connect |kə nĕkt′| *v.* To join: *will connect the parts.* **connects, connected, connecting, connective, connection, connector**

consent |kən sĕnt′| *n.* Approval or agreement: *has her consent to leave. v.* To give approval or permission: *will consent to the plan.* **consents, consented, consenting**

content |kən tĕnt′| *adj.* Pleased: *to be content to wait here.* **contents, contented, contentedly, contentment**

contract |kŏn′trăkt| *n.* An agreement between two or more people, often involving an exchange of work or goods: *agreed to the new contract.* **contracts, contracted, contracting, contractor, contraction**

control |kən trōl′| *n.* The power to guide: *has control of the car.* **controls, controlled, controlling, controllable, controller**

copies |kŏp′ēz| *n.* More than one copy: *five copies of the report.* [see *copy*]

copper |kŏp′ər| *n.* A reddish-brown element found in various ores: *a ring made of copper.* **coppered, coppery**

copy |kŏp'ē| *n.* A thing that is made just like another: *a copy of the letter.* **copies, copied, copying, copier**

costume |kŏs'tōōm'| *n.* The clothes a person wears for disguise or when playing a part: *a costume for the actor.* **costumes, costumed, costuming**

cough |kôf| *n.* The act of air being forced from the lungs suddenly: *a cough and a sneeze.* **coughs, coughed, coughing**

couldn't |kŏŏd'nt| Contraction for *could not:* *couldn't sing.*

county |koun'tē| *n.* In the United States, one of the divisions of a state: *the sheriff of the county.* **counties**

course |kôrs| *n.* **1.** The direction taken: *strayed from their course.* **2.** An area for sports: *racing course.* **courses, coursed**

court |kôrt| *n.* A place where decisions on legal cases are made: *if the court rules favorably.* **courts, courted, courting**

cousin |kŭz'ən| *n.* The child of one's aunt or uncle: *a younger cousin.* **cousins**

coward |kou'ərd| *n.* A person who has no courage or is easily frightened: *ran away like a coward.* **cowards, cowardly, cowardliness**

crawl |krôl| *v.* To move on hands and knees: *will crawl into the cave.* **crawls, crawled, crawling, crawler**

crazy |krā'zē| *adj.* Unusual, foolish, or insane: *a crazy way to drive.* **crazier, craziest, crazily, craziness**

creek |krēk| *n.* A small stream of water that usually leads to a river: *swimming in the creek.* **creeks**

crop |krŏp| *n.* The amount of plants grown for use as food in a single season: *this year's wheat crop.* **crops, cropped, cropping**

crops |krŏps| *n.* A variety of plants grown for use as food: *crops of barley and corn.* [see *crop*]

crouch |krouch| *v.* To bend deeply at the knees: *to crouch under the low beam.* **crouches, crouched, crouching**

crowd |kroud| *n.* A large number of people gathered together: *a crowd of football fans.* **crowds, crowded, crowding**

crowded |kroud'ĭd| *adj.* Filled with many people: *crowded store.* [see *crowd*]

crush |krŭsh| *v.* To press with enough force to break: *will crush the old cans and boxes.* **crushes, crushed, crushing, crushable, crusher**

current |kûr'ənt| *n.* A flow of air or liquid: *a swift current of cold, icy water.* **currents, currently**

cut |kŭt| *v.* To form, divide, or open with a sharp tool: *will cut the bread.* **cuts, cutting, cutter**

cute |kyōōt| *adj.* Pretty: *a cute child.* **cuter, cutest, cutely, cuteness**

cutting |kŭt'ĭng| *v.* Forming, dividing, or opening with a sharp tool: *is cutting the cake.* [see *cut*]

D

daily |dā'lē| *adj.* Done or appearing every day or weekday: *daily newspaper.* [see *day*]

dark |därk| *adj.* With very little or no light: *the dark cave.* **darker, darkest, darken, darkens, darkened, darkening, darkness**

darkness |därk'nĭs| *n.* Very little or no light: *the darkness before dawn.* [see *dark*]

daughter |dô'tər| *n.* One's female child: *son and daughter.* **daughters**

ă pat / ā pay / â care / ä father / ĕ pet / ē be / ĭ pit / ī pie / î fierce / ŏ pot / ō go / ô paw, for / oi oil / ŏŏ book / ōō boot / ou out / ŭ cut / û fur / *th* the / th thin / hw which / zh vision / ə ago, item, pencil, atom, circus
©1977 by Houghton Mifflin Company. Reprinted by permission from THE AMERICAN HERITAGE SCHOOL DICTIONARY.

day |dā| *n.* The time of light between one night and the next: *a long summer day.* **days, daily, dailies**

deaf |dĕf| *adj.* Unable to hear: *deaf person.* **deafen, deafens, deafening, deafness**

deal |dēl| *v.* To give out playing cards: *to deal the entire deck.* **deals, dealt, dealing, dealings, dealer**

dealing |dē'lĭng| *v.* Giving out playing cards: *dealing eight cards to a player.* [see *deal*]

decide |dĭ sīd'| *v.* To make up one's mind; make a decision: *to decide on the answer.* **decides, decided, deciding, decision**

deed |dēd| *n.* An act or a thing done: *a deed for charity.* **deeds, deeded**

delay |dĭ lā'| *v.* To put off until a later time: *to delay the game.* **delays, delayed, delaying**

delayed |dĭ lād'| *v.* Put off until a later time: *delayed his arrival by two hours.* [see *delay*]

depart |dĭ pärt'| *v.* To leave: *will depart at noon.* **departs, departed, departing, departure**

depend |dĭ pĕnd'| *v.* To rely on or trust: *will depend on the coach for help.* **depends, depended, depending, dependable, dependably, dependence, dependency, dependent**

desert |dĕz'ərt| *n.* A dry, sandy region without trees: *camels on the desert.* **deserts, deserted, deserting, deserter, desertion**

differ |dĭf'ər| *v.* To be unlike: *to differ in opinion.* **differs, differed, differing, different, differently, difference**

different |dĭf'ər ənt| *adj.* Unlike or separate: *different from other animals.* [see *differ*]

direct |dĭ rĕkt'| *v.* To conduct, manage, or guide: *can direct the orchestra.* **directs, directed, directing, director, directly, direction, directional, directness**

ditch |dĭch| *n.* A long, narrow trench dug in the earth: *filled the ditch.* **ditches, ditched, ditching**

divide |dĭ vīd'| *v.* **1.** To perform the mathematical operation of division on a number: *will divide 20 by 5.* **2.** To split up and give out: *to divide the pencils among the fifth-grade students.* **divides, divided, dividing, dividend, divider, division, divisor**

doctor |dŏk'tər| *n.* A person who treats the sick: *the doctor who treated my cold.* **doctors, doctored, doctoring**

doesn't |dŭz'ənt| Contraction for *does not: doesn't need help.*

dollar |dŏl'ər| *n.* A unit of money in the United States, equal to 100 cents: *a dollar for the pen.* **dollars**

don't |dōnt| Contraction for *do not: if you don't leave now.*

double |dŭb'əl| *adv.* Two together: *rode double on the ski lift. adj.* Twice as much: *double amount.* **doubles, doubled, doubling, doubly**

downstairs |doun'stârz'| *adv.* To or on a lower floor: *will go downstairs.*

dozen |dŭz'ən| *n.* Twelve: *will buy a dozen.* **dozens**

draw |drô| *v.* To sketch or paint: *will draw a picture.* **draws, drew, drawn, drawing, drawer**

drawing |drô'ĭng| *adj.* For drawing: *the drawing markers. v.* Sketching or painting: *is drawing your portrait.* [see *draw*]

drawn |drôn| *v.* Sketched or painted: *has drawn several trees.* [see *draw*]

dress |drĕs| *n.* Clothes: *in warm dress.* **dresses, dressed, dressing, dresser, dressers**

dresser |drĕs'ər| *n.* A chest of drawers for clothes: *shirts in the dresser.* [see *dress*]

dried |drīd| *adj.* Without wetness: *a dried grape. v.* Got rid of wetness: *dried the clothes outside.* [see *dry*]

drop |drŏp| *v.* To fall or let fall: *will drop the hot potato.* **drops, dropped, dropping, dropper**

dropped |drŏpt| *v.* Let fall: *dropped the eggs.* [see *drop*] dry |drī| adj. Not wet or damp: *dry clothes. v.* To get rid of wetness: *to dry the dishes.* **dries, dried, drying, drier, driest, dryly, dryness**

due |dōō| *adj.* Expected: *if the plane is due soon.* **dues**

duties |dōō'tēz| *n.* Tasks: *duties of the job.* [see *duty*]

duty |dōō'tē| *n.* What a person should do: *your duty to help with the housework.* **duties, dutiful, dutifully**

E

east |ēst| *n.* The direction of the sunrise: *toward the east.* **eastern, easterner, eastward, easterly**

eastern |ē'stərn| *adj.* Of, in, toward, or from the east: *eastern border.* [see *east*]

easy |ē'zē| *adj.* Not needing much effort: *easy task to complete.* **easier, easiest, easily, easiness**

edge |ĕj| *n.* The point where something begins or ends: *the edge of the cliff.* **edges, edged, edging, edgy**

eighteen |ā'tēn'| *adj.* Eight more than ten: *eighteen roses.* **eighteenth, eighteenths**

eighty |ā'tē| *adj.* Eight times ten: *eighty days.* **eighties, eightieth**

elbow |ĕl'bō| *n.* The joint between the lower and the upper arm: *scraped my elbow.* **elbows**

electricity |ĭ lĕk trĭs'ĭ tē| *n.* A form of energy in subatomic particles, able to produce light, motion, and heat: *a car run by electricity.* **electric, electrical, electrify, electrifies, electrified, electrifying, electrocute, electrician**

elephant |ĕl'ə fənt| *n.* A large mammal with a long trunk and ivory tusks: *the tusks on an elephant.* **elephants**

else |ĕls| *adj.* More; besides: *someone else to help.*

empty |ĕmp'tē| *adj.* Containing nothing: *an empty glass.* **empties, emptied, emptying, emptiness**

engine |ĕn'jən| *n.* A machine that turns energy into motion: *car engine.* **engines, engineer, engineers, engineered, engineering**

England |ĭng'glənd| *n.* The largest part of Great Britain: *a large stone castle in England.* **English**

English |ĭng'glĭsh| *n.* The language spoken in England, the United States, Canada, and many other countries: *learned to speak English.* [see *England*]

enough |ĭ nŭf'| *n.* The amount needed or wanted: *more than enough for me.*

enter |ĕn'tər| *v.* To go or come into: *will enter the room.* **enters, entered, entering, entrance**

entered |ĕn'tərd| *v.* Went or came into: *entered the cave.* [see *enter*]

entire |ĕn tīr'| *adj.* Whole or total: *raining the entire day.* **entirely, entirety**

envied |ĕn'vēd| *v.* Desired what someone else has: *envied his artistic talent.* [see *envy*]

envy |ĕn'vē| *v.* To desire what someone else has: *to envy her basketball skill.* **envies, envied, envying, envious, enviously**

erect |ĭ rĕkt'| *v.* To build: *will erect a home.* *adj.* Up straight: *erect posture.* **erects, erected, erecting, erectly**

escape |ĭ skāp'| *v.* To get away from a place of imprisonment or danger: *to escape from jail.* *n.* The act of leaving a place of imprisonment or danger: *the daring escape from the castle.* **escapes, escaped, escaping, escapee, escapist**

ă pat / ā pay / â care / ä father / ĕ pet / ē be / ĭ pit / ī pie / î fierce / ŏ pot / ō go / ô paw, for / oi oil / ōō book / ōō boot / ou out / ŭ cut / û fur / th the / th thin / hw which / zh vision / ə ago, item, pencil, atom, circus

everywhere |ĕv′rē hwâr′| *adv.* In all places: *searched everywhere.*

except |ĕk sĕpt′| *prep.* Other than: *everyone except me.* **excepts, excepted, excepting, exception, exceptional, exceptionally**

excite |ĭk sīt′| *v.* To stir up the feelings of: *will excite her curiosity.* **excites, excited, exciting, excitedly, excitement, excitable**

exciting |ĭk sī′tĭng| *adj.* Stirring or creating excitement: *an exciting adventure story.* [see *excite*]

excuse |ĭk skyoōs′| *n.* A true or untrue reason that is given: *an excuse for leaving school early.* **excuses, excused, excusing, excusable**

export |ĕk′spôrt| *n.* Articles sent out of a country for sale in another country: *an export of beef. v.* To send articles out of a country for sale in another country: *will export a ton of grain.* **exports, exported, exporting, exporter, exportation**

F

fact |făkt| *n.* Something known to be true: *proved this to be a fact.* **facts, factual, factually**

factory |făk′tə rē| *n.* A building where goods are made: *clothing factory.* **factories**

faint |fānt| *v.* To lose consciousness for a short time: *will faint from the heat.* **faints, fainted, fainting, fainter, faintest, faintly**

fair |fâr| *adj.* Honest and just: *a fair decision.* **fairs, fairer, fairest, fairly, fairness**

fairly |fâr′lē| *adv.* Honestly and justly: *spoke fairly of her.* [see *fair*]

false |fôls| *adj.* Not true: *a false statement.* **falsely, falsify, falsified, falsifying, falsehood**

fame |fām| *n.* The fact of being well-known: *the actor's fame.* **famed, famous, famously**

families |făm′ə lēz| *n.* More than one family: *two new families on the street.* [see *family*]

family |făm′ə lē| *n.* Parents and their children: *large family.* **families**

famous |fā′məs| *adj.* Well-known: *a famous author.* [see *fame*]

fancy |făn′sē| *adj.* Decorated; not plain: *fancy clothes.* **fancies, fancied, fancying, fancier, fanciest, fanciful**

fare |fâr| *n.* The price charged to ride a bus, train, airplane, etc.: *money for cab fare.* **fares, fared, faring**

fasten |făs′ən| *v.* To join, connect, or tie together: *will fasten the shoelaces.* **fastens, fastened, fastening, fastener**

favor |fā′vər| *n.* An act of kindness: *returned the favor.* **favors, favored, favoring, favorable, favorably, favoritism, favorite**

fear |fîr| *v.* To be afraid of: *to fear snakes.* **fears, feared, fearing, fearful, fearfully, fearless**

fearful |fîr′fəl| *adj.* Frightened or scared: *was fearful of thunder and lightning.* [see *fear*]

feather |fĕth′ər| *n.* One of the light growths that cover a bird's skin: *a pigeon feather.* **feathers, feathered, feathering, feathery**

festival |fĕs′tə vəl| *n.* A time of merriment, rejoicing, and feasting, in memory of an important event: *a spring festival.* [see *festive*]

festive |fĕs′tĭv| *adj.* Happy or merry: *a festive occasion.* **festively, festivity, festival, festivals**

fifteen |fĭf **tēn'**| *n.* The number after fourteen: *a box of fifteen.* **fifteenth, fifteenths**

fifteenth |fĭf **tēnth'**| *n.* One of fifteen equal parts: *the fifteenth in line. adj.* Next after the fourteenth: *the fifteenth time.* [see *fifteen*]

fifth |fĭfth| *n.* One of five equal parts: *a fifth of the pie. adj.* Next after the fourth: *their fifth pet.* [see *five*]

file |fīl| *v.* To sort books, papers, etc., in a useful order: *will file the accident reports.* **files, filed, filing, filer**

filing |fī'lĭng| *v.* Sorting books, papers, etc., in a useful order: *filing dental records.* [see *file*]

final |fī'nəl| *adj.* Last in a series: *the final chapter in the book.* **finals, finally, finalize, finalist**

fine |fīn| *adj.* Excellent; very good: *a fine job.* **fines, fined, fining, finer, finest**

finest |fī'nĭst| *adj.* The best or the most excellent: *the finest china.* [see *fine*]

finger |fĭng'gər| *n.* One of the five body parts that extend from the hand: *a ring for your finger.* **fingers, fingered, fingering**

finish |fĭn'ĭsh| *n.* An end: *reached the finish last. v.* To reach the end of: *will finish the book tomorrow.* **finishes, finished, finishing, finisher**

fir |fûr| *adj.* Of firs: *fir forest. n.* An evergreen tree: *planted a fir.* **firs**

five |fīv| *n.* The number after four: *a group of five.* **fifth, fifths**

flashlight |flăsh'līt'| *n.* A small, portable lamp, operated by batteries: *flashlight in the tent.* **flashlights**

flew |floo| *v.* Moved through air with wings: *flew to Denver.* [see *fly*]

flight |flīt| *n.* **1.** An airplane that makes scheduled trips: *will board the next flight.* **2.** A set of steps or stairs leading from one floor or landing to the next: *one flight up.* **flights**

flood |flŭd| *n.* A great flow of water over what is usually dry: *a flood near the river.* **floods, flooded, flooding**

fly |flī| *v.* To move through air with wings: *when geese fly.* **flies, flew, flown, flying, flier**

fool |fool| *n.* A person who acts in a silly manner or without sense: *a fool to drive so fast.* **fools, fooled, fooling, foolish, foolishly, foolishness**

foolish |foo'lĭsh| *adj.* In a silly manner; without sense: *foolish action.* [see *fool*]

forbid |fər bĭd'| *v.* To order not to do: *to forbid me from staying up late.* **forbids, forbade, forbidding, forbidden**

forever |fôr ĕv'ər| *n.* A length of time that never ends: *strong enough to last forever.*

form |fôrm| *v.* To make or shape: *will form the clay.* **forms, formed, forming, formal, formally, formalize, formality, formation**

formed |fôrmd| *v.* Made or shaped: *formed the cans into a pyramid.* [see *form*]

forward |fôr'wərd| *adv.* Ahead: *moving forward.* **forwards, forwarded, forwarding, forwardness**

foul |foul| *n.* An unfair play in sports: *a foul in left field. adj.* In sports, against the rules of the game: *foul ball.* **fouls, fouled, fouling, foulest**

fountain |foun'tən| *n.* An upward jet of water: *threw coins into the fountain.* **fountains**

freckle |frĕk'əl| *n.* A small brown spot on the skin: *one freckle on her nose.* **freckles, freckled, freckling**

freckles |frĕk'əlz| *n.* More than one freckle: *freckles on my arms.* [see *freckle*]

free |frē| *adj.* Not under control of another: *free country.* **frees, freed, freeing, freely, freedom**

freedom |frē'dəm| *n.* The state of being free: *freedom from fear.* [see *free*]

ă pat / ā pay / â care / ä father / ĕ pet / ē be / ĭ pit / ī pie / î fierce / ŏ pot / ō go / ô paw, for / oi oil / oo book /
oo boot / ou out / ŭ cut / û fur / th the / th thin / hw which / zh vision / ə ago, item, pencil, atom, circus
©1977 by Houghton Mifflin Company. Reprinted by permission from THE AMERICAN HERITAGE SCHOOL DICTIONARY.

freeze |frēz| v. 1. To become solid by cold: *since water will freeze quickly.* 2. To become perfectly still: *will suddenly freeze in your tracks.* **freezes, froze, freezing, frozen, freezer**

friend |frĕnd| n. A person one knows or likes: *a kind, helpful friend.* **friends, friendly, friendlier, friendliest, friendliness, friendless, friendship**

friendly |frĕnd'lē| adj. Kind; of a friend: *a friendly smile.* [see *friend*]

fright |frīt| n. Sudden terror or fear: *frozen in fright.* **frights, frighten, frightens, frightened, frightening, frightful**

frozen |frō'zən| adj. Turned solid by cold: *frozen vegetables.* [see *freeze*]

further |fûr'thər| adv. At or to a greater amount or extent: *won't speak further.* **furthers, furthered, furthering, furthest, furthermore**

G

gain |gān| v. To increase in weight: *did gain five pounds.* n. An increase: *a gain of ten points.* **gains, gained, gaining, gainful, gainfully**

gallon |găl'ən| n. A liquid measure equal to four quarts: *a gallon of milk.* **gallons**

garage |gə räzh'| n. A building where cars are parked: *two cars in the garage.* **garages, garaged, garaging**

gasoline |găs'ə lēn'| n. A fuel made from petroleum or from gas in the earth: *gasoline for the engine.*

gather |găth'ər| v. To come together in a group: *will gather in the gym for the basketball game.* **gathers, gathered, gathering, gatherings, gatherer**

gathering |găth'ər ĭng| v. Coming together in a group: *are gathering in the park.* n. A group of people: *a gathering of students.* [see *gather*]

general |jĕn'ər əl| adj. Not detailed or precise: *only a general plan.* n. The highest ranking army officer: *a general reviewing the troops.* **generals, generally, generality, generalization**

golf |gŏlf| n. An outdoor game played on a course having nine or eighteen holes spaced far apart. The player uses clubs to hit a ball into one hole after another, taking as few strokes as possible: *clubs for playing golf.* **golfs, golfing, golfer**

good |gŏod| adj. Kind: *a good person.* **goodness**

goodness |gŏod'nĭs| interj. An exclamation that shows surprise: *Oh my goodness!* n. Kindness: *from the goodness of my heart.* [see *good*]

govern |gŭv'ərn| v. To rule through accepted laws: *to govern the people.* **governs, governed, governing, government, governor, governors**

grace |grās| n. Ease and beauty of manner or movement: *dances with grace.* **graces, graced, gracing, graceful, gracefulness, gracefully, graceless, gracelessly**

grandfather |grănd'fä'thər| n. The father of one's father or mother: *worked with my grandfather.* **grandfathers**

grape |grāp| n. A berrylike fruit that grows in bunches on woody vines: *ripe grape.* **grapes**

grapefruit |grāp'frŏot'| n. A round yellow citrus fruit: *peeled the grapefruit.* **grapefruits**

grapes |grāps| n. More than one grape: *purple grapes.* [see *grape*]

grasp |grăsp| n. A strong, firm hold: *a grasp on the steering wheel.* **grasps, grasped, grasping**

gravel |grăv'əl| adj. Made of gravel: *gravel path.* n. Pebbles and small pieces of rock: *a driveway of gravel.* **gravels, graveled, graveling, gravelly**

graze |grāz| v. To feed on live grass: *will graze in the meadow.* **grazes, grazed, grazing**

great |grāt| *adj.* Big in size, amount, or extent: *the great lion.* **greater, greatest, greatly, greatness**

greatest |grā′tĭst| *adj.* Biggest in size, amount, or extent: *picked the greatest watermelon.* [see *great*]

group |grōōp| *n.* A number of persons or things gathered together: *a group of men.* **groups, grouped, grouping**

groups |grōōps| *n.* More than one group: *groups of numbers.* [see *group*]

grow |grō| *v.* To become larger: *will grow from the bud.* **grows, grew, growing, grown, growth, grower**

growl |groul| *n.* An angry rumbling sound: *the lion's growl of pain.* **growls, growled, growling, growler**

growth |grōth| *n.* The amount that has become bigger: *growth of two inches since last week.* [see *grow*]

guard |gärd| *n.* A person who watches over or protects another person or a place: *the king's trusted guard.* **guards, guarded, guarding**

guide |gīd| *v.* To direct or show the way: *will guide the campers. n.* Someone who leads the way: *the museum guide.* **guides, guided, guiding, guidance**

gulf |gŭlf| *n.* An arm of an ocean or sea that is partly surrounded by land: *a cool breeze from the gulf.* **gulfs**

H

hadn't |hăd′nt| Contraction for *had not: hadn't a chance of winning.*

Halloween |hăl′ō ēn′| *adj.* Of or for Halloween: *Halloween treats. n.* The evening of October 31, observed by children playing pranks and asking for treats: *costume for Halloween.*

handful |hănd′fōol′| *n.* The amount that can be held in one's hand: *handful of raisins and nuts.* **handfuls**

handsome |hăn′səm| *adj.* Good-looking: *a handsome suit.* **handsomer, handsomest, handsomely, handsomeness**

harbor |här′bər| *n.* A coastal area of water used to shelter boats: *sailed into the crowded harbor.* **harbors, harbored, harboring**

hardware |härd′wâr′| *adj.* Of or related to hardware: *hardware supplies. n.* Articles made of metal: *hardware in the toolbox.* **hardwares**

harvest |här′vĭst| *n.* The gathering of crops: *a harvest of grain.* **harvests, harvested, harvesting, harvester**

hasn't |hăz′nt| Contraction for *has not: hasn't any idea.*

hatch |hăch| *n.* A group of young brought forth from eggs: *a hatch of turtles. v.* To come out of an egg at birth: *will hatch from the eggs soon.* **hatches, hatched, hatching, hatchery**

headquarters |hĕd′kwôr′tərz| *n.* An office from which a commander sends orders: *police headquarters.*

health |hĕlth| *n.* A person's physical condition: *in good health.* **healthy, healthier, healthiest, healthful, healthiness**

heap |hēp| *n.* A large pile of things thrown one on another: *a heap of clothes.* **heaps, heaped, heaping**

heavy |hĕv′ē| *adj.* Difficult to lift; not light: *carried the heavy suitcase.* **heavier, heaviest, heavily, heaviness**

helmet |hĕl′mĭt| *n.* A covering of sturdy material worn to protect the head: *put on an astronaut's space helmet.* **helmets, helmeted**

ă pat / ā pay / â care / ä father / ĕ pet / ē be / ĭ pit / ī pie / î fierce / ŏ pot / ō go / ô paw, for / oi oil / ŏŏ book / ōō boot / ou out / ŭ cut / û fur / *th* the / th thin / hw which / zh vision / ə ago, item, pencil, atom, circus

©1977 by Houghton Mifflin Company. Reprinted by permission from THE AMERICAN HERITAGE SCHOOL DICTIONARY.

help |hĕlp| *v.* To aid; do what is useful: *will help me clean the house.* **helps, helped, helping, helpful, helpfully, helpfulness, helpless**

helpful |hĕlp′fəl| *adj.* Providing aid; useful: *a helpful worker.* [see *help*]

herd |hûrd| *n.* A group of one kind of animal that stay or are kept together: *a herd of cows.* **herds, herded, herding, herder**

holiday |hŏl′ ĭ dā′| *n.* A day when one does not work: a day to celebrate an event, person, etc.: *a holiday at the ocean.* **holidays**

honest |ŏn′ĭst| *adj.* Truthful and fair: *an honest judge.* **honestly, honesty**

horizon |hə rī′zən| *n.* The line where the earth and sky appear to meet: *the sun sinking below the horizon.* **horizons, horizontal, horizontally**

horizontal |hôr′ĭ zŏn′tl| *adj.* Flat or level: *a horizontal sheet of rock.* [see *horizon*]

hose |hōz| *n.* A tube of flexible material used for carrying liquid over short distances: *the garden hose.* **hoses, hosed, hosing**

household |hous′hōld′| *adj.* Of a household: *household chores. n.* All the people living together in a house or residence: *a happy household.* **households, householder**

however |hou ĕv′ər| *adv.* No matter how: *however busy you are.*

howl |houl| *n.* A shout or a long, loud cry: *a howl of pain.* **howls, howled, howling, howler**

husband |hŭz′bənd| *n.* A man who is married: *the husband of that woman.* **husbands**

I'd |īd| Contraction for *I should, I would,* or *I had: if I'd wait.*

ideal |ī dē′əl| *adj.* Perfect: *an ideal day for tennis.* **ideals, ideally, idealism, idealist, idealistic**

I'll |īl| Contraction for *I will* or *I shall: when I'll leave.*

improve |ĭm prōōv′| *v.* To make or do better: *to improve your chances of winning.* **improves, improved, improving, improvement**

improved |ĭm prōōvd′| *v.* Made or did better: *improved her skill.* [see *improve*]

industry |ĭn′də strē| *n.* All of manufacturing, business, and trade: *a city with declining industry.* **industries, industrious, industrial, industrialist, industrialism**

inform |ĭn fôrm′| *v.* To give facts or knowledge to: *will inform us of your plans.* **informs, informed, informing, informative, information, informational, informer**

information |ĭn′fər mā′shən| *n.* Facts or knowledge received or given: *information on farming.* [see *inform*]

install |ĭn stôl′| *v.* To set in place or adjust for use: *will install the washing machine.* **installs, installed, installing, installation, installment**

intend |ĭn tĕnd′| *v.* To plan or have in mind: *to intend to start early.* **intends, intended, intending**

intent |ĭn tĕnt′| *n.* An aim or purpose: *good intent.* **intents, intently, intention, intentional, intentionally**

interest |ĭn′tər ĭst| *n.* Curiosity: *an interest in whales.* **interests, interested, interesting, interestingly**

invent |ĭn vĕnt′| *v.* To make up or discover for the first time: *to invent a gasless car.* **invents, invented, inventing, inventive, inventiveness, inventor, invention**

invite |ĭn vīt′| *v.* To ask someone to take part in something: *to invite friends to a special birthday party.* **invites, invited, inviting, invitation**

iron |ī′ərn| *v.* To smooth clothing with a heated iron: *will iron the shirt.* **irons, ironed, ironing**

ironing |ī′ər nĭng| *n.* Clothing to be ironed: *a stack of ironing. v.* Smoothing clothing with a heated iron: *ironing a dress.* [see *iron*]

161

item |ī′təm| *n.* A single object or piece: *selected each item very carefully.* ***items, itemize, itemized, itemizing***

I've |īv| Contraction for *I have: when I've gone to the store.*

juicy |jōo′sē| *adj.* Full of juice: *juicy peach.* [see *juice*]

jungle |jŭng′gəl| *n.* An area thickly overgrown with tropical trees and plants: *tigers in the jungle.* ***jungles***

junior |jōo′nyər| *n.* A student in the next-to-last year of high school or college: *a junior in our school. adj.* Made up of or for younger people: *junior membership.* ***Jr., juniors***

J

jacket |jăk′ĭt| *n.* A short coat: *fur jacket.* ***jackets***

jelly |jĕl′ē| *n.* A soft, clear food made by boiling fruit juice and sugar with a thickener: *toast with jelly.* ***jellies, jellied, jell, jells, jelled, jelling***

joke |jōk| *n.* Something done or said to cause laughter: *a silly joke.* ***jokes, joked, joking, jokingly, joker***

jokes |jōks| *n.* More than one joke: *laughed at all her jokes.* [see *joke*]

judge |jŭj| *v.* To decide or settle a contest or issue: *to judge the tennis match. n.* A person who watches over a contest and decides the winner: *the judge on the game show.* ***judges, judged, judging, judgment***

juice |jōos| *n.* The liquid in meat, vegetables, or fruits: *orange juice.* ***juices, juicy, juicier, juiciest, juiciness***

K

kettle |kĕt′l| *n.* A metal pot for boiling liquids: *kettle of soup.* ***kettles***

kitchen |kĭch′ən| *adj.* Related to a kitchen: *kitchen stove. n.* A room where food is cooked: *the stove in the kitchen.* ***kitchens***

knife |nīf| *n.* A flat metal blade fastened to a handle and used for spreading or cutting: *the butter knife.* ***knives, knifed, knifing***

knives |nīvz| *n.* More than one knife: *steak knives.* [see *knife*]

knock |nŏk| *n.* A noise made by a hit: *a light knock on the door.* ***knocks, knocked, knocking, knocker***

know |nō| *v.* **1.** To have the facts about: *to know the problem.* **2.** To be aware of: *does know the danger of fire.* ***knows, knew, knowing, knowingly, known, knowledge***

knowing |nō′ĭng| *n.* Awareness: *because knowing isn't always believing. adj.* Having awareness or knowledge: *a knowing scholar.* [see *know*]

ă pat / ā pay / â care / ä father / ĕ pet / ē be / ĭ pit / ī pie / î fierce / ŏ pot / ō go / ô paw, for / oi oil / ōo book / ōo boot / ou out / ŭ cut / û fur / *th* the / th thin / hw which / zh vision / ə ago, item, pencil, atom, circus
©1977 by Houghton Mifflin Company. Reprinted by permission from THE AMERICAN HERITAGE SCHOOL DICTIONARY.

known |nōn| v. Been aware of: *had known the outcome.* adj. Accepted in general: *known for his honesty.* [see *know*]

L

ladies |lā'dēz| n. More than one lady: *the ladies on the committee.* [see *lady*]

lady |lā'dē| n. Any woman referred to in a polite way: *the lady in charge.* **ladies**

language |lăng'gwĭj| adj. Of languages: *language class.* n. The speech and writing that a nation or a particular group uses to communicate: *learned a new language.* **languages**

large |lârj| adj. Big: *a large apple.* **larger, largest, largely, largeness**

largely |lärj'lē| adv. Mostly: *largely to blame.* [see *large*]

leather |lĕth'ər| n. The cleaned, tanned skin of an animal: *leather for shoes.* **leathers, leathered, leathery**

lemon |lĕm'ən| adj. Flavored with lemon: *lemon cookies.* n. A yellow citrus fruit: *lemon for the tea.* **lemons, lemony**

lemonade |lĕm'ə nād'| n. A drink made by mixing lemon juice, water, and sugar: *lemonade on a hot day.*

liberty |lĭb'ər tē| n. Freedom; independence: *fought for our country's liberty and justice.* **liberties, liberate, liberates, liberated, liberating, liberation, liberator**

limb |lĭm| n. A large branch of a tree: *the limb that broke.* **limbs, limber**

limp |lĭmp| n. An irregular way of walking that results from an injured leg: *the patient's limp.* **limps, limped, limping, limper**

line |līn| v. To sew a layer of cloth inside a jacket, dress, etc.: *will line the wool coat.* **lines, lined, lining, liner**

lining |lī'nĭng| n. The layer of cloth inside a jacket, dress, etc.: *the jacket's satin lining.* [see *line*]

listen |lĭs'ən| v. To try to hear something: *will listen to the speech.* **listens, listened, listening, listener**

live |līv| adj. Alive: *live plant.* **lively, livelier, liveliest, lives, lived, living, livable, lifeless, life**

lively |līv'lē| adj. Filled with life or action: *a lively crowd.* [see *live*]

load |lōd| v. To put cargo in or on: *will load ten boxes onto the truck.* **unload, unloads, unloaded, unloading**

loaf |lōf| v. To spend time doing nothing: *to loaf all day indoors.* **loafs, loafed, loafing, loafer**

loafing |lō'fĭng| n. The act of spending time doing nothing: *a Saturday for loafing.* [see *loaf*]

loan |lōn| n. Money lent to be paid back with interest: *a loan to make home repairs.* **loans, loaned, loaning**

lodge |lŏj| n. A countrylike house where people stay for short periods of time: *a ski lodge.* **lodges, lodged, lodging, lodger**

lone |lōn| adj. Being without others: *a lone star in the sky.* **lonely, lonelier, loneliest, loneliness, loner, lonesome**

lonely |lōn'lē| adj. Sad at being without others: *lonely child away from home.* [see *lone*]

lonesome |lōn'səm| adj. Sad at being without others: *lonesome man.* [see *lone*]

loose |loōs| adj. Not tight or fastened: *loose sweater.* **looses, loosed, loosing, loosen, loosens, loosened, loosening, looser, loosest, loosely, looseness**

M

machine |mə shēn'| n. A device that uses energy to perform a task: *sewing machine.* **machines, machinery, machinist**

magazine |măg′ə zēn′| *adj.* Of or for magazines: *magazine stand.* *n.* A publication of stories and articles, issued regularly: *sports magazine.* **magazines**

maintain |mān tān′| *v.* To keep up: *to maintain a friendship.* **maintains, maintained, maintaining, maintenance**

married |măr′ēd| *v.* Brought together as wife and husband: *married today.* [see *marry*]

marry |măr′ē| *v.* To bring together as wife and husband: *will marry the couple.* **marries, married, marrying, marriage**

match |măch| *n.* A piece of wood or cardboard coated at one end with a mixture that catches fire when rubbed on a rough or special surface: *a match to light the oven.* **matches, matched, matching, matchless**

matches |măch′ĭz| *n.* More than one match: *box of kitchen matches.* [see *match*]

mayor |mā′ər| *n.* The person who heads the government of a city or town: *was elected mayor.* **mayors, mayoral**

meadow |mĕd′ō| *n.* Grassy land, usually used for growing hay or as pasture: *cows in the meadow.* **meadows**

meantime |mēn′tīm′| *n.* The same time: *in the meantime.* *adv.* At the same time: *Meantime, listen carefully.*

meanwhile |mēn′hwīl′| *n.* The same time: *in the meanwhile.* *adv.* At the same time: *Meanwhile, rest here.*

member |mĕm′bər| *n.* A person who belongs to a group: *member of the club.* **members, membership**

mention |mĕn′shən| *n.* The act of speaking about or referring to: *a mention of your work.* *v.* To speak about or refer to: *will mention my name.* **mentions, mentioned, mentioning, mentionable**

merchant |mûr′chənt| *n.* A person who buys and sells to make a profit: *goods from the local merchant.* **merchants, merchandise**

message |mĕs′ĭj| *n.* Spoken or written words sent from one person to another: *a message to call home.* **messages, messenger, messengers**

midnight |mĭd′nīt′| *n.* Twelve o'clock at night: *arrived at midnight.* [see *night*]

million |mĭl′yən| *adj.* One thousand thousand: *a million people.* *n.* A number equal to one thousand thousand: *counted to a million.* **millions, millionth, millionaire**

minute |mĭn′ĭt| *n.* Sixty seconds: *one minute ago.* **minutes**

mirror |mĭr′ər| *n.* A glass surface that reflects images clearly: *saw himself in the mirror.* **mirrors, mirrored, mirroring**

mistake |mĭ stāk′| *n.* An error: *a mistake on the test.* **mistakes, mistook, mistaking, mistaken, mistakenly, mistakable**

model |mŏd′l| *adj.* Built as a small-scale copy: *a model plane.* *n.* A small-scale copy of something: *a model of a sailboat.* **models, modeled, modeling**

moment |mō′mənt| *n.* A very brief space of time: *will wait a moment.* **moments, momentary**

month |mŭnth| *n.* One of the twelve divisions of a year: *month of May.* **months, monthly**

monthly |mŭnth′lē| *adv.* Every month: *visited monthly.* [see *month*]

mood |mood| *n.* A general state of mind or feeling: *in a good mood.* **moods, moody, moodiness**

moss |môs| *n.* Small green plants that form a dense growth on ground, trees, or rocks: *moss on the forest trees.* **mosses, mossy**

motor |mō′tər| *n.* An engine that produces motion: *a motor on the boat.* **motors, motored, motoring, motorize, motorist**

mountain |moun′tən| *adj.* Of mountains: *mountain air.* *n.* A steep hill: *climbed the mountain.* **mountains, mountainous, mountaineer, mountainside**

ă pat / ā pay / â care / ä father / ĕ pet / ē be / ĭ pit / ī pie / î fierce / ŏ pot / ō go / ô paw, for / oi oil / o͞o book /
o͞o boot / ou out / ŭ cut / û fur / th the / th thin / hw which / zh vision / ə ago, item, pencil, atom, circus
©1977 by Houghton Mifflin Company. Reprinted by permission from THE AMERICAN HERITAGE SCHOOL DICTIONARY.

mud |mŭd| *n.* Wet earth that is soft and sticky: *stuck in the mud.* **muddy, muddies, muddied, muddying, muddier, muddiest**

muddy |mŭd'ē| *adj.* Covered with mud: *muddy floor.* [see *mud*]

multiply |mŭl'tə plī| *v.* To add a number to itself a certain number of times: *will multiply 16 by 20.* **multiplies, multiplied, multiplying, multiple, multiplication, multiplier**

music |myoo'zĭk| *n.* The art of combining sounds that are pleasing or meaningful to a listener: *the loud music of the band.* **musical, musically, musician**

musician |myoo zĭsh'ən| *n.* A person skilled in the performance or composition of music: *the musician at the piano.* [see *music*]

N

nation |nā'shən| *n.* The land occupied by a country: *a small nation in Europe.* **nations, national, nationally, nationalist, nationality**

nature |nā'chər| *n.* Everything except anything made by human beings: *the beauties of nature.* **natures, natured, natural, naturally, naturalness**

naughty |nô'tē| *adj.* Bad: *a naughty way to act.* **naughtier, naughtiest, naughtily, naughtiness**

navy |nā'vē| *n.* **1.** A dark-blue color: *a dress of navy.* **2.** The branch of a nation's armed forces organized for sea warfare: *trained in a navy.* **navies, naval**

nearby |nîr'bī'| *adj.* Close by: *nearby forest.*

necktie |nĕk'tī'| *n.* A narrow piece of cloth worn under a shirt collar and tied in front: *silk necktie.* **neckties**

needle |nē'dl| *n.* **1.** A slender sewing tool, pointed at one end and with a hole in the other end to pass a thread through: *sewing needle.* **2.** A slender rod, usually used in pairs, for knitting: *plastic knitting needle.* **needles, needled, needling**

neighbor |nā'bər| *n.* A person who lives next door or nearby: *the neighbor to the left.* **neighbors, neighboring, neighborly, neighborliness, neighborhood, neighborhoods**

neighborhood |nā'bər hood'| *n.* The people living in a particular area: *neighborhood of adults.* [see *neighbor*]

nephew |nĕf'yoo| *n.* The son of a person's brother or sister: *his oldest nephew.* **nephews**

newspaper |nooz'pā'pər| *n.* A daily or weekly publication printed on large paper and containing articles, pictures, advertisements, etc.: *the newspaper lying on the front porch.* **newspapers**

newspapers |nooz'pā pərz| *n.* More than one newspaper: *five different newspapers.* [see *newspaper*]

night |nīt| *n.* The hours of darkness between sunset and sunrise: *a rainy night.* **nights, nightly, midnight, midnights**

nine |nīn| *n.* The number after eight: *a total of nine.* **nines, ninth, ninths**

ninth |nīnth| *adj.* After the eighth: *the ninth child.* [see *nine*]

north |nôrth| *n.* The direction to the right of the setting sun: *snow to the north.* **northern, northerner, northerly, northward**

northern |nôr'thərn| *adj.* Of, in, toward, or from the north: *traveled to the northern district.* [see *north*]

O

odd |ŏd| *adj.* Of whole numbers that cannot be evenly divided by 2: *the odd numbers 33 and 11.* **odds, odder, oddest, oddly, oddness, oddity**

offer |ô'fər| *n.* Something presented as a suggestion, plan, or proposal: *an offer of advice.* **offers, offered, offering**

often |ô′fən| *adv.* Frequently: *went there often.* ***oftener, oftenest***

operate |ŏp′ə rāt′| *v.* **1.** To control the running of a machine: *can operate the bulldozer.* **2.** To perform surgery: *will operate on the patient.* ***operates, operated, operating, operator, operation, operational***

orchard |ôr′chərd| *n.* An area in which fruit trees are grown: *an apple orchard.* ***orchards***

order |ôr′dər| *v.* To command or tell what to do: *will order you to leave.* ***orders, ordered, ordering, orderly***

ordered |ôr′dərd| *v.* Commanded or told what to do: *ordered the carpenters to keep working.* [see *order*]

ore |ôr| *n.* A mineral containing metal for which it is mined: *ore in the mine.* ***ores***

organ |ôr′gən| *n.* A musical instrument whose sound is produced by air blown through pipes when keys are struck: *played the organ.* ***organs, organist***

outline |out′līn′| *n.* A drawing of only the outer edge of something: *drew an outline of the house.* ***outlines, outlined, outlining***

overcome |ō′vər kŭm′| *adj.* Exhausted or made helpless: *was overcome with much sadness.* ***overcomes, overcame, overcoming***

overturn |ō′vər tûrn′| *v.* To turn upside down: *if the boat will overturn.* ***overturns, overturned, overturning***

owe |ō| *v.* **1.** To have to give a sum of: *to owe money.* **2.** To have a duty to give: *does owe us an explanation for being late.* ***owes, owed, owing***

P

pajamas |pə jä′məz| *n.* A loose shirt and trousers worn for sleeping: *striped flannel pajamas.*

palace |păl′ĭs| *adj.* Related to a palace: *the palace guard.* *n.* The official home of a royal person: *the queen's palace.* ***palaces***

palm |päm| *n.* **1.** The inside surface of the hand, between the fingers and the wrist: *many lines on your palm.* **2.** A tree with a tall trunk, leaves at the top, and no branches: *tried to grow a palm in the yard.* ***palms, palmed, palming, palmist, palmistry***

parade |pə rād′| *n.* A march or procession: *a parade on the Fourth of July.* ***parades, paraded, parading***

pardon |pär′dn| *n.* Forgiveness: *begged his pardon.* ***pardons, pardoned, pardoning, pardonable***

parent |pâr′ənt| *n.* A father or mother: *one signature from either parent.* ***parents, parental***

parents |pâr′ənts| *n.* One's father and mother: *the parents of that child.* [see *parent*]

parties |pär′tēz| *n.* More than one party: *several holiday parties.* [see *party*]

partner |pärt′nər| *n.* One of two or more persons involved in an activity: *my skating partner.* ***partners, partnership***

party |pär′tē| *n.* An event for which a group of people are gathered together to have fun: *a party for the new graduates.* ***parties, partied, partying***

passenger |păs′ən jər| *n.* One who rides in, but does not drive, a vehicle: *passenger on a bus.* ***passengers***

pasture |păs′chər| *n.* Grassland on which animals graze: *pasture for the farm animals.* *v.* To graze on grassland: *if the sheep pasture until the sun sets.* ***pastures, pastured, pasturing***

ă pat / ā pay / â care / ä father / ĕ pet / ē be / ĭ pit / ī pie / î fierce / ŏ pot / ō go / ô paw, for / oi oil / ŏŏ book / ōō boot / ou out / ŭ cut / û fur / *th* the / th thin / hw which / zh vision / ə ago, item, pencil, atom, circus
©1977 by Houghton Mifflin Company. Reprinted by permission from THE AMERICAN HERITAGE SCHOOL DICTIONARY.

patch |păch| *n.* A small area that is different from the area around it: *a patch of burned grass.* *v.* To cover and repair a hole in something with something else: *will patch the potholes in the road.* **patches, patched, patching**

pay |pā| *v.* To give money to for goods or for work done: *will pay their grocery bills.* **pays, paid, paying, payable, payment, payments**

payment |pā′mənt| *n.* An amount paid: *made a weekly payment.* [see *pay*]

peace |pēs| *n.* Freedom from war or disorder: *peace after war.* **peaceful, peacefully, peacefulness**

people |pē′pəl| *n.* Human beings: *friendly people.* **peoples, peopled, peopling**

perfume |pûr′fyo̅o̅m′| *n.* A liquid with a sweet smell: *perfume that smells like roses.* **perfumes, perfumed, perfumer**

perhaps |pər hăps′| *adv.* Possibly; maybe: *will perhaps win.*

period |pîr′ē əd| *n.* The punctuation mark used at the end of some sentences and after most abbreviations: *a period or a question mark.* **periods, periodical, periodically**

person |pûr′sən| *n.* A human being: *a friendly person.* **persons, personal, personally, personalize, personable, personality**

piano |pē ăn′ō| *n.* A keyboard musical instrument sounded by a hammer striking a wire when a key is struck: *sat at the piano.* **pianos, pianist**

piece |pēs| *n.* A part of something that has been broken or divided: *piece of apple pie.* **pieces, pieced, piecing**

pilgrim |pĭl′grĭm| *n.* A traveler: *pilgrim on a journey.* **pilgrims, pilgrimage**

pilgrims |pĭl′grĭmz| *n.* Travelers: *pilgrims heading east.* [see *pilgrim*]

pitch |pĭch| *v.* To throw or toss: *to pitch to the batter.* **pitches, pitched, pitching, pitcher, pitchers**

pitcher |pĭch′ər| *n.* The baseball player who throws, or pitches, the ball to the batter: *our team's pitcher.* [see *pitch*]

plain |plān| *adj.* Simple; not fancy: *plain clothing.* **plainer, plainest, plainly, plainness**

plan |plăn| *v.* To think out ahead of time what is to be made or done: *will plan a vacation for next fall.* **plans, planned, planning, planner**

planning |plăn′ĭng| *v.* Thinking out ahead of time what is to be made or done: *planning a cookout for Saturday.* [see *plan*]

plantation |plăn tā′shən| *n.* A large farm or estate on which workers tend the crops and often live on the same property: *a cotton plantation.* **plantations**

plastic |plăs′tĭk| *n.* A chemically made substance that is easily molded or shaped: *a car made of plastic.* **plastics**

platform |plăt′fôrm′| *n.* A raised, horizontal surface: *platform for the musicians.* **platforms**

popular |pŏp′yə lər| *adj.* Liked by many: *a popular book.* **popularly, popularity**

potato |pə tā′tō| *n.* An oval, starchy vegetable with a thin skin: *a boiled potato for the stew.* **potatoes**

powder |pou′dər| *n.* A substance of very tiny particles: *a box of talcum powder.* **powders, powdered, powdering**

practice |prăk′tĭs| *v.* To do many times over to gain skill: *will practice piano lessons daily.* **practices, practiced, practicing**

practicing |prăk′tĭs ĭng| *v.* Doing many times over to gain skill: *was practicing my pitching.* [see *practice*]

praise |prāz| *n.* Words that express admiration; a compliment: *won praise for her piano playing.* **praises, praised, praising**

preach |prēch| *v.* To lecture or speak to: *will preach about good health.* **preaches, preached, preaching, preacher**

prepare |prĭ pâr′| *v.* To make or get ready: *to prepare the dinner.* **prepares, prepared, preparing, preparation**

preparing |prĭ pâr′ĭng| *v.* Making or getting ready: *preparing to leave.* [see *prepare*]

president |prĕz′ĭ dənt| *n.* The chief executive of a republic: *was president for four years.* ***presidents, presidential, presidency***

prince |prĭns| *n.* The son of a king or queen: *prince of this country.* ***princes, princely, princess***

print |prĭnt| *v.* To form letters or words as they are in printed material: *should print the two messages on white paper.* ***prints, printed, printing, printer***

printing |prĭn′tĭng| *n.* Letters or words as they are in printed material: *neat and even printing.* —**Printing press**— A machine for rapidly printing the same material onto many sheets of paper. [see *print*]

probable |prŏb′ə bəl| *adj.* Likely to occur: *a probable result.* ***probably, probability***

probably |prŏb′ə blē| *adv.* Most likely: *is probably correct.* [see *probable*]

problem |prŏb′ləm| *n.* **1.** A troubling question or situation: *the problem of always being late.* **2.** A question to be solved by mathematics: *a hard problem on the math test.* ***problems, problematic***

product |prŏd′əkt| *n.* **1.** Something made to be sold: *sold the product to a customer.* **2.** An answer from multiplying: *the product of 10 times 20.* ***products, produce, produces, produced, producing, productive, production***

products |prŏd′əkts| *n.* **1.** Things made to be sold: *farm products.* **2.** Answers from multiplying: *the products of 2 times 4 and 3 times 8.* [see *product*]

program |prō′grăm| *n.* A plan of what will be done or presented: *followed a program of daily exercise.* ***programs, programmed, programming, programmer***

promise |prŏm′ĭs| *n.* A declaration binding a person to do or not to do something; a vow: *a promise to be on time.* ***promises, promised, promising***

pronounce |prə nouns′| *v.* To make the sounds of by speech: *to pronounce French perfectly.* ***pronounces, pronounced, pronouncing, pronunciation***

protect |prə tĕkt′| *v.* To shelter from harm or danger: *seat belts to protect you.* ***protects, protected, protecting, protective, protection, protector***

protest |prə tĕst′| *v.* To express objection to something: *to protest the lawyer's comment on the robbery case.* ***protests, protested, protesting, protester***

prove |proōv| *v.* To show that something is true: *will prove I am right.* ***proves, proved, proving, proven, proof***

proving |proō′vĭng| *v.* Showing that something is true: *is proving the statement.* [see *prove*]

public |pŭb′lĭk| *n.* The people as a whole: *for the public to decide.* ***publicly, publicize, publicity***

pumpkin |pŭmp′kĭn| *n.* A large, round fruit used as a vegetable or for pies: *12-pound pumpkin.* ***pumpkins***

pupil |pyoō′pəl| *n.* A student: *the kindergarten pupil.* ***pupils***

put |poŏt| *v.* To set or place: *will put the dishes on the table.* —**Put on**— To clothe oneself with. ***puts, putting***

putting |poŏt′ĭng| *v.* Setting or placing: *is putting books in a stack.* [see *put*]

puzzle |pŭz′əl| *n.* A problem or task to be solved for fun: *a wooden puzzle.* ***puzzles, puzzled, puzzling, puzzler***

Q

quart |kwôrt| *n.* A liquid measure equal to one fourth of a gallon: *quart of apple juice.* ***quarts***

ă pat / ā pay / â care / ä father / ĕ pet / ē be / ĭ pit / ī pie / î fierce / ŏ pot / ō go / ô paw, for / oi oil / oŏ book / oō boot / ou out / ŭ cut / û fur / th the / th thin / hw which / zh vision / ə ago, item, pencil, atom, circus
©1977 by Houghton Mifflin Company. Reprinted by permission from THE AMERICAN HERITAGE SCHOOL DICTIONARY.

quarter |kwôr′tər| *n.* A coin worth 25 cents: *a quarter for the bus ride home.* **quarters, quartered, quartering, quarterly**

quest |kwĕst| *n.* A search: *a quest for truth.* **quests, quested, questing**

question |kwĕs′chən| *n.* Something asked in order to get information: *a difficult question to answer.* **questions, questioned, questioning, questionable, questionably, questionnaire, questioner**

quick |kwĭk| *adj.* Fast: *a quick walk.* **quicker, quickest, quickly, quickness**

quickly |kwĭk′lē| *adv.* Rapidly: *moving quickly toward us.* [see *quick*]

R

racket |răk′ĭt| *n.* An oval frame with interlaced strings and a handle, used in sports to strike a ball: *squash racket.* **rackets**

rag |răg| *n.* A piece of old, torn, or leftover cloth: *a rag for cleaning.* **rags, ragged, raggedly, raggedness**

ragged |răg′ĭd| *adj.* **1.** Rough or uneven: *ragged piece of metal.* **2.** Tattered or worn: *ragged clothes.* [see *rag*]

raise |rāz| *v.* To lift to a higher place: *will raise the shelf one foot above the table.* **raises, raised, raising**

rank |răngk| *n.* A position or class: *in the third rank.* *v.* To put in an order; rate: *to rank the students' grades.* **ranks, ranked, ranking**

rare |râr| *adj.* **1.** Not usual: *a rare butterfly.* **2.** Cooked so the inside is still red: *barbecuing rare steak for dinner.* **rarer, rarest, rarely, rareness, rarity**

reach |rēch| *v.* **1.** To arrive at: *will reach the top of the hill.* **2.** To stretch out a hand for something: *can reach the glass of milk.* **reaches, reached, reaching, reachable**

reached |rēcht| *v.* **1.** Stretched out a hand for something: *reached for his coat.* **2.** Arrived at: *reached our destination.* [see *reach*]

reaches |rē′chĭz| *v.* **1.** Arrives at: *reaches the top of the stairs.* **2.** Stretches out a hand for something: *reaches for the ball.* [see *reach*]

real |rē′əl| *adj.* True or actual: *the real story.* **really, realistic, realize, reality, realist, realization**

really |rē′ə lē| *adv.* Truly or actually: *is really happening.* [see *real*]

reason |rē′zən| *n.* **1.** An explanation: *your reason for being late.* **2.** A cause for an action or feeling: *the reason for your happiness.* **reasons, reasoned, reasoning, reasonable, reasonably**

recess |rē′sĕs′| *n.* A period of time when normal activity is stopped: *an hour's recess from working.* **recesses, recessed, recessing, recession**

record |rĕk′ərd| *n.* **1.** A flat, grooved vinyl disk to be played on a phonograph: *a record of piano music.* **2.** The best rate, amount, speed, etc., that has been reached: *broke the record for the 100-yard dash.* **records, recorded, recording, recorder**

regular |rĕg′yə lər| *adj.* Usual or normal: *regular visit.* **regularly, regularity, regulate, regulates, regulated, regulating, regulation**

remain |rĭ mān′| *v.* To stay or continue to stay in a place: *will remain in your seats during the test.* **remains, remained, remaining, remainder**

remark |rĭ märk′| *n.* A short statement; comment: *a funny remark.* **remarks, remarked, remarking, remarkable, remarkably**

remarkable |rĭ mär′kə bəl| *adj.* Worthy of comment; astounding: *a remarkable meteor shower.* [see *remark*]

remember |rĭ mĕm′bər| *v.* To recall or think of again: *will remember the appointment.* **remembers, remembered, remembering, remembrance**

replied |rĭ plīd′| *v.* Answered: *replied too late.* [see *reply*]

reply |rĭ plī′| *v.* To answer: *to reply to a question.* **replies, replied, replying**

ribbon |rĭb′ən| *n.* A strip of satin, velvet, etc., used for tying or decorating things: *a ribbon in her hair.* **ribbons**

rifle |rī′fəl| *n.* A gun, fired from the shoulder, having spiral grooves in the barrel: *officer's rifle.* **rifles, rifled, rifling, rifler, riflery**

rise |rīz| *v.* To go or move upward: *watched the kite rise.* **rises, rose, rising, risen**

risk |rĭsk| *n.* The chance of harm or danger: *to swim at your own risk.* *v.* To take a dangerous chance: *to risk her safety.* **risks, risked, risking, risky, riskier, riskiest**

rooster |rōō′stər| *n.* A full-grown male chicken: *rooster in the barn.* **roosters**

rough |rŭf| *adj.* **1.** Not smooth or even: *rough pavement.* **2.** Without details; incomplete: *a rough idea.* **roughs, roughed, roughing, rougher, roughest, roughly, roughness**

route |rōōt| *n.* A road or course: *the route along the river.* **routes, routed, routing**

ruin |rōō′ĭn| *v.* To destroy or spoil: *will ruin your shirt.* *n.* One or more ancient buildings in terrible condition: *the ruin of the stone bridge.* **ruins, ruined, ruining, ruinous**

rule |rōōl| *v.* **1.** To draw straight lines: *will rule the paper.* **2.** To govern a country: *will be the next king to rule.* **rules, ruled, ruling, ruler, rulers**

rulers |rōō′lərz| *n.* **1.** Straight-edged strips used for measuring or drawing: *used rulers to measure the room.* **2.** People who govern countries: *rulers of many nations.* [see *rule*]

■■■■■■■■ **S** ■■■■■■■■

safe |sāf| *adj.* Free from harm, risk, or danger: *in a safe place.* **safes, safer, safest, safely, safeness, safety**

safely |sāf′lē| *adv.* With care to avoid harm: *was safely crossing the street.* [see *safe*]

safety |sāf′tē| *adj.* Of or for safety: *safety helmet.* *n.* Freedom from harm, risk, or danger: *stayed back for safety.* [see *safe*]

sail |sāl| *v.* To travel on water in a boat that moves by the wind's action on sails: *to sail the Atlantic.* **sails, sailed, sailing, sailor, sailors**

sailor |sā′lər| *n.* A person who is a member of a ship's crew: *more than one sailor on the yacht.* [see *sail*]

salt |sôlt| *n.* A white substance used for food, found in the earth and the sea: *salt for the meat.* **salts, salted, salting, salty, saltier, saltiest**

salty |sôl′tē| *adj.* Full of salt: *salty ham.* [see *salt*]

sample |săm′pəl| *n.* An example from a group that shows what the group is like: *a sample of cloth.* **samples, sampled, sampling, sampler**

savage |săv′ĭj| *adj.* Fierce, brutal, or cruel: *the dog's savage growl.* **savages, savagely, savageness**

save |sāv| *v.* To prevent loss or waste of: *will save money for groceries.* **saves, saved, saving, savings, saver**

savings |sā′vĭngz| *n.* Money saved: *a small savings in the bank.* [see *save*]

scar |skär| *n.* The mark left after a wound has healed: *a scar on my leg.* **scars, scarred, scarring**

scarce |skârs| *adj.* Not in great supply: *scarce water supply.* **scarcer, scarcest, scarcely, scarcity, scarceness**

scare |skâr| *v.* To frighten: *will scare the mouse.* **scares, scared, scaring, scary, scarier, scariest, scarer, scariness**

scarf |skärf| *n.* A piece of fabric worn around the head or neck: *silk scarf.* **scarves**

ă pat / ā pay / â care / ä father / ĕ pet / ē be / ĭ pit / ī pie / î fierce / ŏ pot / ō go / ô paw, for / oi oil / ŏŏ book /
ōō boot / ou out / ŭ cut / û fur / *th* **the** / th thin / hw which / zh vision / ə ago, item, pencil, atom, circus
©1977 by Houghton Mifflin Company. Reprinted by permission from THE AMERICAN HERITAGE SCHOOL DICTIONARY.

schoolmate |skōōl′māt′| *n.* A companion at school: *library books for my schoolmate.* **schoolmates**

scorn |skôrn| *v.* To look down on: *To scorn their advice.* **scorns, scorned, scorning, scornful, scornfully, scornfulness**

scowl |skoul| *n.* An angry look or frown: *directed a scowl at the noisy audience.* **scowls, scowled, scowling, scowler**

seal |sēl| *v.* To close tight, as with glue or wax: *to seal the package. n.* A sea mammal with flippers: *the trained seal.* **seals, sealed, sealing, sealer**

seashore |sē′shôr′| *n.* The land near the edge of the sea: *shells along the seashore.* **seashores**

secret |sē′krĭt| *n.* Something kept hidden from others: *knows a secret. adj.* Hidden from others: *a secret hiding place.* **secrets, secretive, secretly, secrecy**

secure |sĭ kyŏŏr′| *v.* To fasten firmly: *will secure all the doors.* **secures, secured, securing, securely, security**

select |sĭ lĕkt′| *v.* To choose: *will select a book to buy.* **selects, selected, selecting, selective, selection**

sentence |sĕn′təns| *n.* A group of words, containing a subject and a predicate, that express a complete thought: *to punctuate the sentence.* **sentences, sentenced, sentencing**

settle |sĕt′l| *v.* To choose a place to live and make a home there: *to settle in a new city.* **settles, settled, settling, settlement, settler**

sew |sō| *v.* To use a needle and thread: *will sew a button on the shirt.* **sews, sewed, sewn, sewing**

shack |shăk| *n.* A small, roughly built cabin: *an old shack in the woods.* **shacks**

shadow |shăd′ō| *n.* Shade made by a person, animal, or object: *a long shadow at dusk. v.* To throw shade on: *trees that shadow the house.* **shadows, shadowed, shadowing, shadowy**

shake |shāk| *v.* 1. To move or cause to move quickly to and fro, back and forth, or up and down: *will shake the juice.* 2. To clasp hands to greet, congratulate, etc.: *will shake your hand if you win.* **shakes, shook, shaking, shaken, shaky, shaker**

shame |shām| *n.* An uncomfortable feeling for having done something wrong: *felt shame when lying.* **shames, shamed, shaming, shameless, shameful, ashamed, ashamedly**

shelter |shĕl′tər| *n.* Protection: *a shelter from the cold. v.* To protect: *to shelter your eyes from the bright sun.* **shelters, sheltered, sheltering**

shook |shŏŏk| *v.* Moved or caused to move quickly: *shook out the rugs.* [see *shake*]

shop |shŏp| *v.* To look at or buy things in a store: *to shop for food.* **shops, shopped, shopping, shopper**

shopping |shŏp′ĭng| *adj.* Of looking at or buying things in a store: *a shopping spree. v.* Looking at or buying things in a store: *was shopping for clothes.* [see *shop*]

shovel |shŭv′əl| *n.* A tool with a long handle and a flattened scoop, used to lift and throw matter: *a snow shovel.* **shovels, shoveled, shoveling, shoveler**

signal |sĭg′nəl| *n.* A sign that gives notice or warning: *a signal to stop.* **signals, signaled, signaling, signaler**

silly |sĭl′ē| *adj.* Senseless or foolish: *a silly joke.* **sillier, silliest, silliness**

skim |skĭm| *v.* To read hastily for only the most obvious: *will skim the book by tomorrow afternoon.* **skims, skimmed, skimming, skimmer**

skin |skĭn| *v.* To injure by scraping: *will skin my legs if I fall on the sidewalk.* **skins, skinned, skinning**

skinned |skĭnd| *v.* Injured by scraping: *skinned his knee on the ice.* [see *skin*]

skirt |skûrt| *n.* A piece of clothing that hangs from the waist but is not divided between the legs: *the plaid skirt.* **skirts, skirted, skirting**

sleeve |slēv| *n.* The part of a garment covering the arm: *sleeve of the jacket.* **sleeves, sleeved, sleeveless**

slip |slĭp| *v.* To lose balance or footing on a slippery surface: *might slip on the ice.* **slips, slipped, slipping, slippery, slipperiness, slipper, slippers**

slipped |slĭpt| *v.* Lost balance or footing on a slippery surface: *slipped on the wet leaves.* [see *slip*]

small |smôl| *adj.* Little: *small building.* **smaller, smallest, smallness**

smaller |smôl′ər| *adj.* Littler: *the smaller child.* [see *small*]

smooth |smo͞oth| *v.* To make something flat or level: *will smooth the covers.* **smooths, smoothed, smoothing, smoothness, smoother, smoothest, smoothly**

soak |sōk| *v.* To let remain in liquid until wet through: *will soak in soapy water.* **soaks, soaked, soaking**

somehow |sŭm′hou′| *adv.* In one way or another: *will begin somehow.*

someone |sŭm′wŭn′| *pron.* Some person: *told someone the story.*

somewhat |sŭm′hwät′| *adv.* Rather; slightly: *is somewhat peculiar.*

somewhere |sŭm′hwĕr′| *adv.* At, in, or to one place or another: *is resting somewhere. n.* An unknown place: *somewhere to rest for the night.*

sour |sour| *adj.* Having a sharp taste: *sour lemon.* **sours, soured, souring, sourest, sourly, sourness**

south |south| *n.* The direction to the left of the setting sun: *warmer to the south.* **southern, southerner, southerly, southward**

southern |sŭth′ərn| *adj.* Of, in, toward, or from the south: *pink clouds in the southern sky.* [see *south*]

sparrow |spăr′ō| *n.* A small gray or brown songbird: *a sparrow on the feeder.* **sparrows**

split |splĭt| *n.* An acrobatic trick in which the legs are spread far apart in opposite directions: *the ballerina who did a split.* **splits, splitting, splitter**

spoon |spo͞on| *n.* An eating utensil consisting of a small shallow bowl and a handle: *spoon for the soup.* **spoons, spooned, spooning**

spray |sprā| *n.* A moving group of water droplets: *the spray of an ocean wave.* **sprays, sprayed, spraying, sprayer**

square |skwâr| *n.* A rectangle with four equal sides: *a four-inch square.* **squares, squared, squaring, squarely, squareness, squarer, squarest, squarish**

squirrel |skwûr′əl| *n.* A gray or reddish-brown rodent with a bushy tail: *the furry squirrel.* **squirrels, squirreled, squirreling**

stack |stăk| *n.* A large pile of something: *a stack of dishes.* **stacks, stacked, stacking**

stalk |stôk| *n.* The main stem of a plant: *a stalk of wheat.* **stalks, stalked, stalking**

station |stā′shən| *n.* **1.** A place that transmits radio or television signals: *a radio station.* **2.** A regular stopping place along a route: *boarded at the last station.* **stations, stationed, stationing, stationary**

stoop |sto͞op| *v.* To bend forward and downward: *will stoop to get into the cave.* **stoops, stooped, stooping**

straight |strāt| *adj.* Free from bends or curves: *straight road.* **straighter, straightest, straighten, straightens, straightened, straightening, straightener**

strain |strān| *v.* **1.** To pull hard: *to strain in the tug-of-war.* **2.** To push through a strainer: *will strain the orange juice.* **strains, strained, straining, strainer**

ă **pat** / ā **pay** / â **care** / ä **father** / ĕ **pet** / ē **be** / ĭ **pit** / ī **pie** / î **fierce** / ŏ **pot** / ō **go** / ô **paw, for** / oi **oil** / o͝o **book** /
o͞o **boot** / ou **out** / ŭ **cut** / û **fur** / *th* **the** / th **thin** / hw **which** / zh **vision** / ə **ago, item, pencil, atom, circus**
©1977 by Houghton Mifflin Company. Reprinted by permission from THE AMERICAN HERITAGE SCHOOL DICTIONARY.

stray |strā| *v.* To wander from the right course: *to stray from the marked path.* **strays, strayed, straying**

strike |strīk| *v.* To hit hard: *to strike the nail with a hammer.* **strikes, struck, striking, striker**

strip |strip| *n.* A narrow, flat piece of something: *a strip of paper for a bookmark. v.* To pull off; remove: *will strip the sheets from the bed.* **strips, stripped, stripping**

struck |strŭk| *v.* Hit hard: *struck by a hurricane.* [see *strike*]

stubborn |stŭb'ərn| *adj.* Difficult to deal with or manage: *a stubborn knot.* **stubborner, stubbornest, stubbornly, stubbornness**

student |stoōd'nt| *n.* A person who attends a school: *new student in our class.* **students**

studies |stŭd'ēz| *v.* Learns facts or ideas about a subject: *studies the lesson.* [see *study*]

study |stŭd'ē| *v.* To learn facts or ideas about a subject: *to study for the test.* **studies, studied, studying, studious**

stuff |stŭf| *v.* To pack too fully: *to stuff the red suitcase with clothes.* **stuffs, stuffed, stuffing, stuffy**

stump |stŭmp| *n.* The lower part of a tree, left after the main part is cut off: *a stump that is covered with moss.* **stumps, stumped, stumping, stumpy**

suit |soōt| *n.* A set of clothing, usually a jacket and trousers or skirt, to be worn together: *gray wool suit.* **—Bathing suit—** A garment worn for swimming. **suits, suited, suiting, suitable**

suits |soōts| *n.* More than one suit: *two striped suits.* [see *suit*]

sun |sŭn| *n.* The star around which all the planets in the solar system revolve: *the planet nearest to the sun.* **suns, sunned, sunning, sunny, sunnier, sunniest, sunniness**

sunny |sŭn'ē| *adj.* **1.** Filled with sunshine: *sunny room.* **2.** Cheerful: *has a sunny personality.* [see *sun*]

sure |shoōr| *adj.* Certain: *sure of the answer.* **surer, surest, surely, sureness**

surely |shoōr'lē| *adv.* Certainly: *surely knows the way.* [see *sure*]

surprise |sər prīz'| *n.* Something not expected: *a surprise for my birthday.* **surprises, surprised, surprising, surprisingly**

surprises |sər prī'zĭz| *n.* More than one surprise: *surprises for the party.* [see *surprise*]

swallow |swŏl'ō| *v.* To cause food or drink to pass down the throat: *to swallow a peanut. n.* Any of several birds with long wings and a forked tail: *the swallow in the barn.* **swallows, swallowed, swallowing**

sway |swā| *v.* To move back and forth: *to sway in the summer breeze.* **sways, swayed, swaying**

sweater |swĕt'ər| *n.* A knitted garment for the upper part of the body: *wool sweater.* **sweaters**

swim |swĭm| *v.* To move through water by using arms, legs, fins, etc.: *to swim in the lake.* **swims, swam, swum, swimming, swimmer**

swimming |swĭm'ĭng| *v.* Moving through water by using arms, legs, fins, etc.: *is swimming to shore.* [see *swim*]

T

tablet |tăb'lĭt| *n.* A pad of paper: *a small tablet for notes.* **tablets**

tackle |tăk'əl| *n.* In football, the act of stopping and throwing to the ground an opponent who has the ball: *a tackle of the quarterback. v.* **1.** To seize: *will tackle him if he tries to escape.* **2.** To undertake or try to deal with: *will tackle the problem later.* **tackles, tackled, tackling, tackler**

talent |tăl'ənt| *n.* A special ability: *a talent for drawing.* **talents, talented**

taught |tôt| *v.* Gave lessons in: *taught French.* [see *teach*]

teach |tēch| *v.* To give lessons in: *will teach science and English.* **teaches, taught, teaching, teacher**

temper |tĕm′pər| *n.* **1.** A mood; state of mind: *an even temper.* **2.** An angry state of mind: *in a bad temper.* **tempers, tempered, tempering**

tennis |tĕn′ĭs| *n.* A sport played by two or four players on a court with a net. The players hit a ball back and forth over the net with a racket: *a three-hour game of tennis.*

thank |thăngk| *v.* To say that one is grateful for something: *will thank them for helping.* **thanks, thanked, thanking, thankful, thankfully, thankless, thanksgiving**

thankful |thăngk′fəl| *adj.* Grateful: *thankful for the meal.* [see *thank*]

threw |thrōō| *v.* Tossed: *threw the ball to first base.* [see *throw*]

thrill |thrĭl| *n.* A sudden, exciting feeling: *a thrill at seeing the tallest building.* **thrills, thrilled, thrilling, thrillingly, thriller**

throat |thrōt| *n.* The passage leading from the mouth to the stomach or lungs: *a sore throat.* **throats, throaty**

throw |thrō| *v.* To toss: *to throw a ball.* **throws, threw, thrown, throwing, thrower**

thumb |thŭm| *n.* The short, thick first finger of the hand: *a cut on her thumb.* **thumbs, thumbed, thumbing**

thunder |thŭn′dər| *n.* The loud noise that follows lightning: *the thunder during the storm.* *v.* To make a noise like thunder: *to thunder through the halls.* **thunders, thundered, thundering**

tie |tī| *v.* To fasten with string, rope, etc.: *will tie the boat to the dock.* **ties, tied, tying**

tied |tīd| *v.* Fastened with string, rope, etc.: *tied his shoes.* [see *tie*]

tomato |tə mā′tō| *n.* A fleshy reddish fruit eaten as a vegetable: *ripe tomato.* **tomatoes**

tone |tōn| *n.* **1.** A sound of a certain quality: *the deep tone of the foghorn.* **2.** A shade of color: *a blue tone in the painting.* **tones, toned, toning, toneless, toner**

tones |tōnz| *n.* **1.** Sounds of a certain quality: *tones of the choir.* **2.** Shades of color: *many red tones in the rug.* [see *tone*]

topic |tŏp′ĭk| *n.* A subject: *the topic for the lecture.* **topics**

toss |tôs| *v.* To move oneself about with force or intensity: *to toss all night while trying to sleep.* **tosses, tossed, tossing**

touch |tŭch| *v.* To feel with part of the body: *to touch the rough rock.* **touches, touched, touching, touchable, touchy**

toward |tôrd| *prep.* In the direction of: *toward the sunset.* **towards**

treasure |trĕzh′ər| *n.* Riches or valuable items: *the treasure in the sunken ship.* **treasures, treasured, treasuring, treasurer, treasury**

troop |trōōp| *v.* To move together in large numbers: *will troop around the flagpole.* **troops, trooped, trooping, trooper**

trouble |trŭb′əl| *n.* Difficulty, pain, or worry: *caused trouble in class.* **troubles, troubled, troubling, troublesome**

trout |trout| *n.* A freshwater fish: *to fish for trout.* **trouts**

truth |trōōth| *n.* A statement proven to be accepted as true: *a scientific truth.* **truths, truthful, truthfully, truthfulness**

U

ugly |ŭg′lē| *adj.* **1.** Dangerous: *ugly fire.* **2.** Unpleasant to look at: *ugly picture.* **uglier, ugliest, ugliness**

ă pat / ā pay / â care / ä father / ĕ pet / ē be / ĭ pit / ī pie / î fierce / ŏ pot / ō go / ô paw, for / oi oil / ōō book / ōō boot / ou out / ŭ cut / û fur / *th* the / th thin / hw which / zh vision / ə ago, item, pencil, atom, circus
©1977 by Houghton Mifflin Company. Reprinted by permission from THE AMERICAN HERITAGE SCHOOL DICTIONARY.

uncle |ŭng′kəl| *n.* The brother of one's mother or father: *the son of my uncle.* **uncles**

uniform |yōō′nə fôrm′| *n.* The outfit worn by group members on duty, by which they may be known as belonging to that group: *the guard's uniform.* **uniforms, uniformed, uniformly**

unit |yōō′nĭt| *n.* One thing or person: *a unit of weight.* **units, unite, unites, united, uniting, unity**

unless |ŭn lĕs′| *conj.* If not; except if: *unless you leave.*

unload |ŭn lōd′| *v.* To remove cargo from: *to unload the trunk.* [see *load*]

unwilling |ŭn wĭl′ĭng| *adj.* Not wishing or desiring: *unwilling to change.* [see *will*]

up |ŭp| *adv.* To a higher place: *when the plane flew up.* **upper**

upper |ŭp′ər| *adj.* Higher: *on the upper shelf.* [see *up*]

usual |yōō′zhōō əl| *adj.* Common or ordinary: *will meet us at the usual place.* **usually, usualness**

usually |yōō′zhōō ə lē| *adv.* Commonly or ordinarily: *usually happy.* [see *usual*]

V

valentine |văl′ən tīn′| *n.* A card or gift given on Valentine's Day: *sent him a valentine.* **valentines**

valley |văl′ē| *n.* A narrow, low land between mountains or hills: *rode into the valley.* **valleys**

view |vyōō| *n.* A scene or something seen: *a view from the roof.* **views, viewed, viewing, viewer**

village |vĭl′ĭj| *adj.* Of or related to a village: *village residents.* *n.* A group of houses and other buildings that form a community smaller than a town: *in the center of the village.* **villages, villager**

visit |vĭz′ĭt| *v.* To go or come to see: *will visit some friends.* **visits, visited, visiting, visitor, visitors**

visitor |vĭz′ĭ tər| *n.* A person who visits; guest: *welcomed the visitor from another country.* [see *visit*]

voice |vois| *n.* The sound made through a person's mouth: *strange voice.* **voices, voiced, voicing, voiceless**

voices |vois′ĭz| *n.* More than one voice: *voices from the audience.* [see *voice*]

vote |vōt| *n.* One's choice in an election: *placing a vote in the ballot box.* **votes, voted, voting, voter**

votes |vōts| *n.* More than one vote: *totaled the votes.* [see *vote*]

W

waist |wāst| *n.* The part of a person's body between the ribs and the hips: *above the waist.* **waists**

water |wô′tər| *v.* To moisten or supply with water: *will water the roses.* **waters, watered, watering, watery**

watered |wô′tərd| *v.* Moistened or supplied with water: *watered the lawn with the sprinkler.* [see *water*]

weather |wĕ *th*′ ər| *n.* The condition of air at a certain time and place: *hot summer weather.*

weigh |wā| *v.* To find out how heavy something is: *will weigh the bag of apples.* **weighs, weighed, weighing, weight, weights, weightless**

we're |wîr| Contraction for *we are*: *when we're ready.*

weren't |wûrnt| Contraction for *were not*: *because we weren't prepared.*

west |wĕst| *n.* The direction of the sunset: *headed toward the west.* **western, westerner, westerly, westward**

western |wĕs′tərn| *adj.* Of, in, toward, or from the west: *the western sky.* [see *west*]

we've |wĕv| Contraction for *we have: when we've arrived.*

whale |hwāl| *n.* A mammal that lives in the sea and looks like a large fish: *a whale near the ship.* **whales, whaling, whaler, whalers**

who |hoo| *pron.* That: *the man who knows you.* **whom, whose**

whole |hōl| *adj.* Complete or entire: *a whole box of books.* **wholes, wholesome, wholly**

whose |hooz| *adj.* Of whom or which: *whose bike I borrowed.* [see *who*]

wicked |wĭk′ĭd| *adj.* Evil or bad: *wicked thoughts.* **wickedly, wickedness**

wild |wīld| *adj.* Untamed; growing or found in a natural state: *wild blueberries.* **wilder, wildest, wildly, wilds, wilderness, wildness**

wilderness |wĭl′dər nĭs| *n.* An unpopulated region in its natural condition: *hiked into the wilderness.* [see *wild*]

will |wĭl| *v.* To desire or wish: *as you will.* **unwilling, unwillingly, unwillingness**

withdraw |wĭth drô′| *v.* To take away; remove: *will withdraw my vote.* **withdraws, withdrew, withdrawn, withdrawing, withdrawal**

wonder |wŭn′dər| *v.* To feel awe, doubt, or surprise: *will wonder at the beautiful sight.* *n.* Something that creates awe or admiration: *a wonder to see.* **wonders, wondered, wondering, wonderful, wonderfully, wondrous**

worse |wûrs| *adj.* Less good: *worse storm than yesterday's.* [see *bad*]

wouldn't |wood′nt| Contraction for *would not: wouldn't want any.*

wrist |rĭst| *n.* The joint where the hand and forearm meet: *broke her wrist playing tennis.* **wrists**

ă pat / ā pay / â care / ä father / ĕ pet / ē be / ĭ pit / ī pie / î fierce / ŏ pot / ō go / ô paw, for / oi oil / oo book / oo boot / ou out / ŭ cut / û fur / *th* the / th thin / hw which / zh vision / ə ago, item, pencil, atom, circus
©1977 by Houghton Mifflin Company. Reprinted by permission from THE AMERICAN HERITAGE SCHOOL DICTIONARY.